Primary

Phonics Intervention Centers

Consonant
Digraphs & Blends

Writing: Camille Liscinsky
Content Editing: De Gibbs
Lisa Vitarisi Mathews
Copy Editing: Cathy Harber
Art Direction: Cheryl Puckett
Cover Design: Liliana Potigian
Illustrator: Cheryl Nobens
Design/Production: Arynne Elfenbein
Kathy Kopp
Yuki Meyer
Marcia Smith

EMC 3522

Evan-Moor®
EDUCATIONAL PUBLISHERS
Helping Children Learn since 1979

Visit
teaching-standards.com
to view a correlation
of this book.
This is a free service.

*Correlated to State and
Common Core State Standards*

For information about other Evan-Moor products, call 1-800-777-4362,
fax 1-800-777-4332, or visit our Web site, www.evan-moor.com.
Entire contents © 2012 EVAN-MOOR CORP.
18 Lower Ragsdale Drive, Monterey, CA 93940-5746. Printed in USA.

Contents

How to Use This Book

The centers in this book are designed to be completed in a small-group setting. All materials are included for groups of up to 6 students. The activities have been carefully crafted to meet the needs of students receiving Tier 2 Response to Intervention instruction, as well as the needs of any other students who are learning foundational phonics skills. The target skills in *Consonant Digraphs and Blends* include recognizing the sounds of frequently used digraphs and blends and applying those sounds to read words.

For the Teacher

Lesson Plan The skills in each unit are taught through teacher-led explicit instruction and are practiced through phonemic-awareness, hands-on, and written activities.

A fully scripted lesson plan cycles through auditory, oral, visual, and hands-on letter-sound activities that help students decode and read new words.

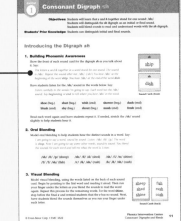
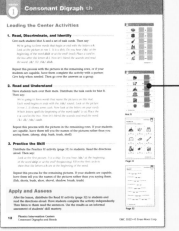

front   *back*

Scaffolded activities help guide students through the lesson.

Sound Cards

Vocabulary cards feature target sounds and aid students in blending sounds to read words.

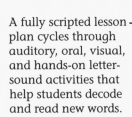
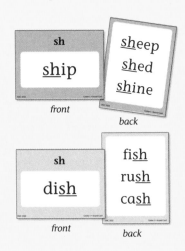

front   *back*

Answer Keys

Each center includes a two-sided page of answer keys, showing mat activities on one side and written application activities on the other side.

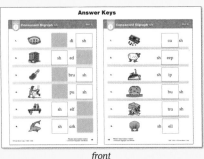
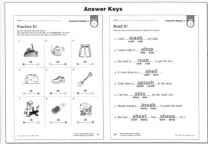

front   *back*

For the Student

Each unit has six sets of activity mats and corresponding task cards, providing individual group members with their own materials for practicing the target skill.

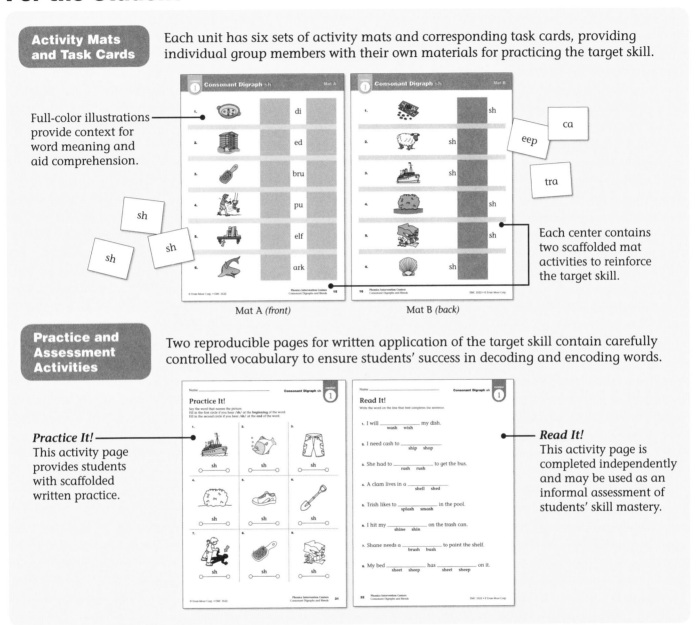

Full-color illustrations provide context for word meaning and aid comprehension.

Mat A *(front)*   Mat B *(back)*

Each center contains two scaffolded mat activities to reinforce the target skill.

Two reproducible pages for written application of the target skill contain carefully controlled vocabulary to ensure students' success in decoding and encoding words.

Practice It!
This activity page provides students with scaffolded written practice.

Read It!
This activity page is completed independently and may be used as an informal assessment of students' skill mastery.

Record Forms

Two reproducible record forms are included for tracking and assessing students' progress, individually or as a group. The *Group Progress Record* provides space for written comments and an assessment of skill mastery for each student in a particular group. The *Student Progress Record* includes a detailed breakdown of each center's objectives to informally assess an individual student's skill mastery.

How to Make and Store the Centers

You Will Need

- pocket-style folders (1 per center)
- business-size envelopes or small, self-locking plastic bags (12 per center)
- scissors, tape, marking pen
- laminating materials and equipment

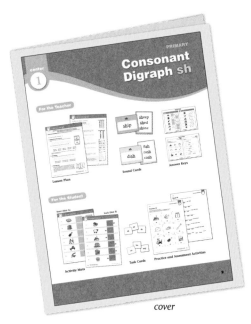

cover

Steps to Follow (for each center)

1. Remove the perforated pages and laminate all color pages. (Do not laminate the *Practice It!* and *Read It!* activities.)

2. Attach the cover page to the front of the folder.

3. Place the lesson plan in the left-hand pocket.

4. Cut apart the sound cards and the set of answer keys and place them with the lesson plan in the left-hand pocket of the folder.

5. Place all activity mats in the right-hand pocket.

6. Cut apart the task cards for Mat A and Mat B and sort them by student number (located on the back of most cards).

7. Keep each set of cards in a separate envelope or plastic bag and place them in the right-hand pocket of the folder.

8. Reproduce one copy of the *Practice It!* and *Read It!* activities for each student and place them in the right-hand pocket of the folder.

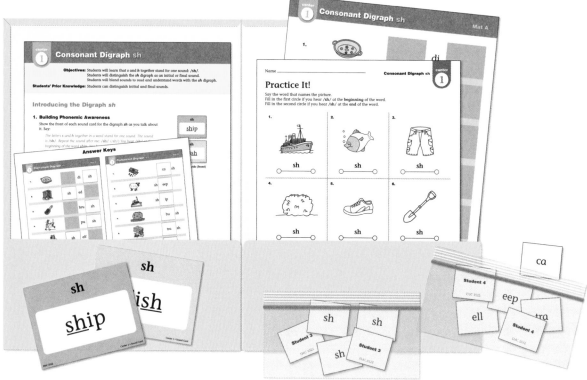

Phonics Intervention Centers
Consonant Digraphs and Blends

Phonics Intervention Centers
Consonant Digraphs and Blends

Group Progress Record

Center _____

Name	Comments	Assessment Level

Phonics Intervention Centers
Consonant Digraphs and Blends

Student Progress Record

Assessment Levels
M = mastered
N = needs more practice
R = reteach

	Date / Assessment	Date / Assessment	Date / Assessment
1 Consonant Digraph *sh*			
Recognizes that the *sh* digraph stands for the /sh/ sound			
Distinguishes the *sh* digraph as an initial or final sound			
Reads and understands words with the *sh* digraph			
2 Consonant Digraph *ch*			
Recognizes that the *ch* digraph stands for the /ch/ sound			
Distinguishes the *ch* digraph as an initial or final sound			
Reads and understands words with the *ch* digraph			
3 Consonant Digraph *th*			
Recognizes that the *th* digraph stands for the /th/ sound			
Distinguishes the *th* digraph as an initial or final sound			
Reads and understands words with the *th* digraph			
4 Consonant Digraphs Review			
Reads and understands words with the digraph *sh*, *ch*, or *th*			
5 Consonant + *r* Blends			
Recognizes the blends *br*, *cr*, *dr*, *fr*, *gr*, *pr*, and *tr*			
Blends individual sounds into words			
Reads and understands words with an initial *r* blend			
6 Consonant + *l* Blends			
Recognizes the blends *bl*, *cl*, *fl*, *gl*, *pl*, and *sl*			
Blends individual sounds into words			
Reads and understands words with an initial *l* blend			
7 Initial *s* Blends			
Recognizes the blends *sc*, *sk*, *sm*, *sn*, *sp*, *st*, and *sw*			
Blends individual sounds into words			
Reads and understands words with an initial *s* blend			
8 Consonant Blends Review			
Reads and understands words with an initial *r*, *l*, or *s* blend			

center 1

Consonant Digraph sh

For the Teacher

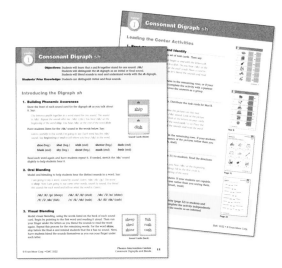

Lesson Plan

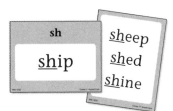

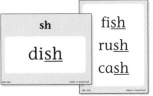

Sound Cards

Answer Keys

For the Student

front (Mat A)

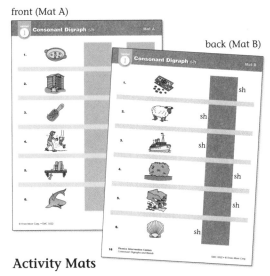

back (Mat B)

Activity Mats

Task Cards

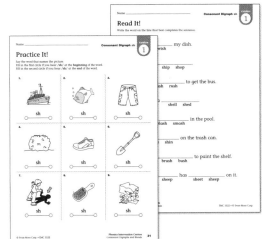

Practice and Assessment Activities

EMC 3522 • © Evan-Moor Corp.

Consonant Digraph **sh**

center 1

Objectives: Students will learn that **s** and **h** together stand for one sound: /sh/.
Students will distinguish the **sh** digraph as an initial or final sound.
Students will blend sounds to read and understand words with the **sh** digraph.

Students' Prior Knowledge: Students can distinguish initial and final sounds.

Introducing the Digraph *sh*

1. Building Phonemic Awareness

Show the front of each sound card for the digraph **sh** as you talk about it. Say:

*The letters **s** and **h** together in a word stand for one sound. The sound is /sh/. Repeat the sound after me: /sh/. (/sh/) You hear /sh/ at the beginning of the word **ship**. You hear /sh/ at the end of the word **dish**.*

Have students listen for the /sh/ sound in the words below. Say:

*Listen carefully to the words I'm going to say. Each word has the /sh/ sound. Say **beginning** or **end** to tell where you hear /sh/ in the word.*

Sound Cards (front)

shoe (beg.)	**shut** (beg.)	**wish** (end)	**shower** (beg.)	**dash** (end)
blush (end)	**shy** (beg.)	**shout** (beg.)	**mash** (end)	**fresh** (end)

Read each word again and have students repeat it. If needed, stretch the /sh/ sound slightly to help students hear it.

2. Oral Blending

Model oral blending to help students hear the distinct sounds in a word. Say:

*I am going to say a word, sound by sound. Listen: /sh/ /ŏ/ /p/. The word is **shop**. Now I am going to say some other words, sound by sound. You blend the sounds for each word and tell me what the word is. Listen:*

/sh/ /ē/ /p/ (sheep)	/sh/ /ĕ/ /d/ (shed)	/sh/ /ī/ /n/ (shine)
/f/ /ĭ/ /sh/ (fish)	/r/ /ŭ/ /sh/ (rush)	/k/ /ă/ /sh/ (cash)

3. Visual Blending

Model visual blending, using the words listed on the back of each sound card. Begin by pointing to the first word and reading it aloud. Then run your finger under the letters as you blend the sounds to read the word again. Repeat this process for the remaining words. For the word **shine**, stop before the final **e** and remind students that the **e** has no sound. Next, have students blend the sounds themselves as you run your finger under each letter.

Sound Cards (back)

Leading the Center Activities

1. Read, Discriminate, and Identify ....

Give each student Mat A and a set of task cards. Then say:

*We're going to form words that begin or end with the letters **s-h**. Look at the picture in row 1. It is a dish. Do you hear /**sh**/ at the beginning of the word **dish** or at the end? (end) Place a card in the box after the letters **d-i**. Now let's blend the sounds and read the word: /d/ /ĭ/ /sh/ **dish**.*

Repeat this process with the pictures in the remaining rows, or if your students are capable, have them complete the activity with a partner. Give help when needed. Then go over the answers as a group.

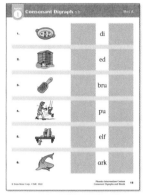

Mat A

2. Read and Understand ....

Have students turn over their mats. Distribute the task cards for Mat B. Then say:

*We're going to form words that name the pictures on this mat. Each word begins or ends with the /**sh**/ sound. Look at the picture in row 1. It shows some cash. Now look at the letters on your cards. Which letters spell the beginning of the word **cash**? (c-a) Place the **c-a** card in the box. Now let's blend the sounds and read the word: /k/ /ă/ /sh/ **cash**.*

Repeat this process with the pictures in the remaining rows. If your students are capable, have them tell you the names of the pictures rather than you saying them. (sheep, ship, bush, trash, shell)

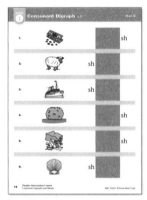

Mat B

3. Practice the Skill ....

Distribute the Practice It! activity (page 31) to students. Read the directions aloud. Then say:

*Look at the first picture. It is a ship. Do you hear /**sh**/ at the beginning of the word **ship** or at the end? (beginning) Fill in the first circle to show that the letters **s-h** are at the beginning of the word.*

Repeat this process for the remaining pictures. If your students are capable, have them tell you the names of the pictures rather than you saying them. (fish, shorts, bush, shoe, shovel, shadow, brush, trash)

Page 31

Apply and Assess

After the lesson, distribute the Read It! activity (page 32) to students and read the directions aloud. Have students complete the activity independently. Then listen to them read the sentences. Use the results as an informal assessment of students' skill mastery.

Page 32

sh

ship

sh

dish

Answer Keys

Consonant Digraph sh — Mat A

center 1

1.	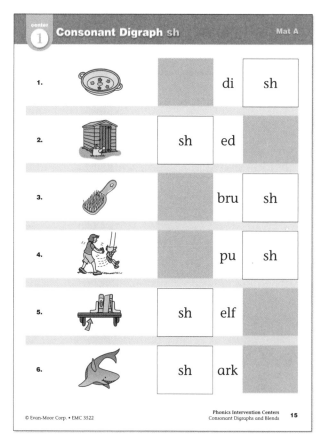		di	sh
2.		sh	ed	
3.			bru	sh
4.			pu	sh
5.		sh	elf	
6.		sh	ark	

Consonant Digraph sh — Mat B

center 1

1.	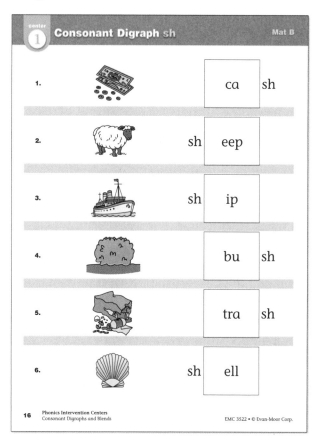	ca	sh
2.		sh	eep
3.		sh	ip
4.		bu	sh
5.		tra	sh
6.		sh	ell

fish

ru<u>sh</u>

ca<u>sh</u>

Center 1 • Sound Card

<u>sh</u>eep

<u>sh</u>ed

<u>sh</u>ine

Center 1 • Sound Card

Answer Keys

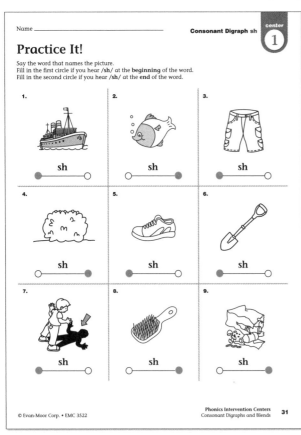

1. di

2. ed

3. bru

4. pu

5. elf

6. ark

1.    sh

2.  sh

3.  sh

4.    sh

5.    sh

6.  sh

1. di

2. ed

3. bru

4. pu

5. elf

6. ark

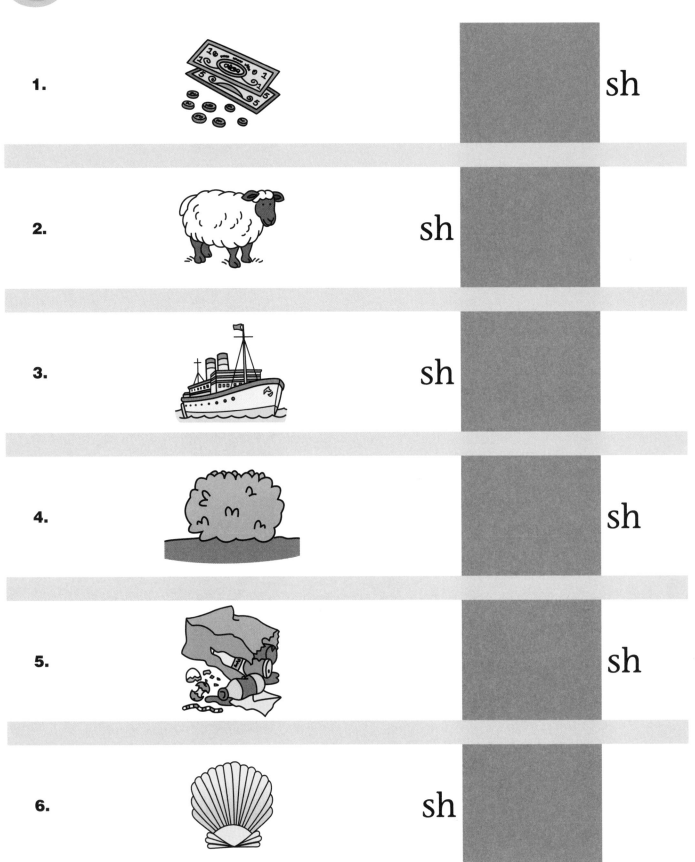

1. sh

2. sh

3. sh

4. sh

5. sh

6. sh

1. di

2. ed

3. bru

4. pu

5. elf

6. ark

1.

sh

2.

sh

3.

sh

4.

sh

5.

sh

6.

sh

Phonics Intervention Centers
Consonant Digraphs and Blends

EMC 3522 • © Evan-Moor Corp.

1.  di

2.  ed

3.  bru

4.  pu

5. elf

6.  ark

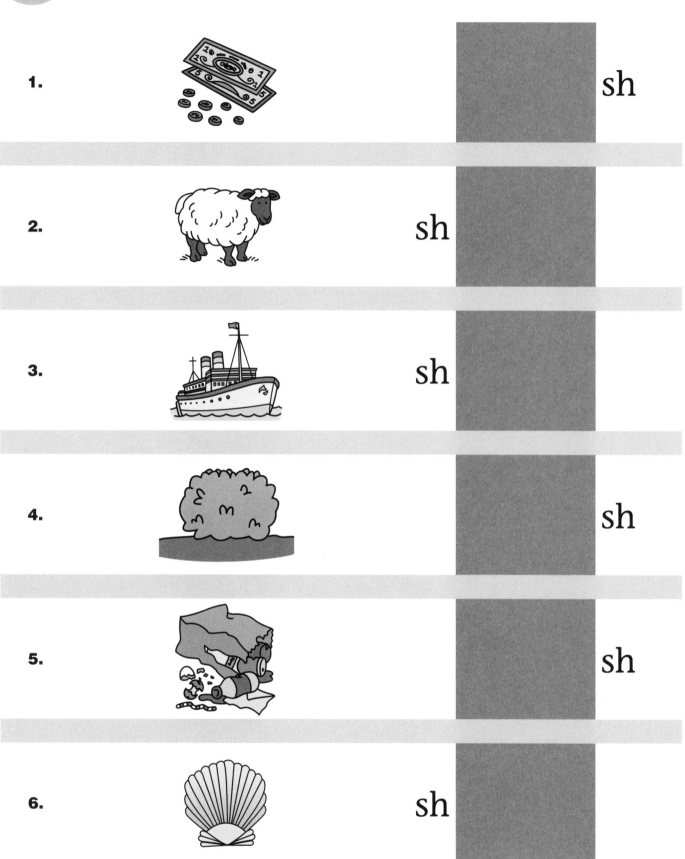

1.   sh

2.   sh

3.   sh

4.   sh

5.   sh

6.   sh

1. di

2. ed

3. bru

4. pu

5. elf

6. ark

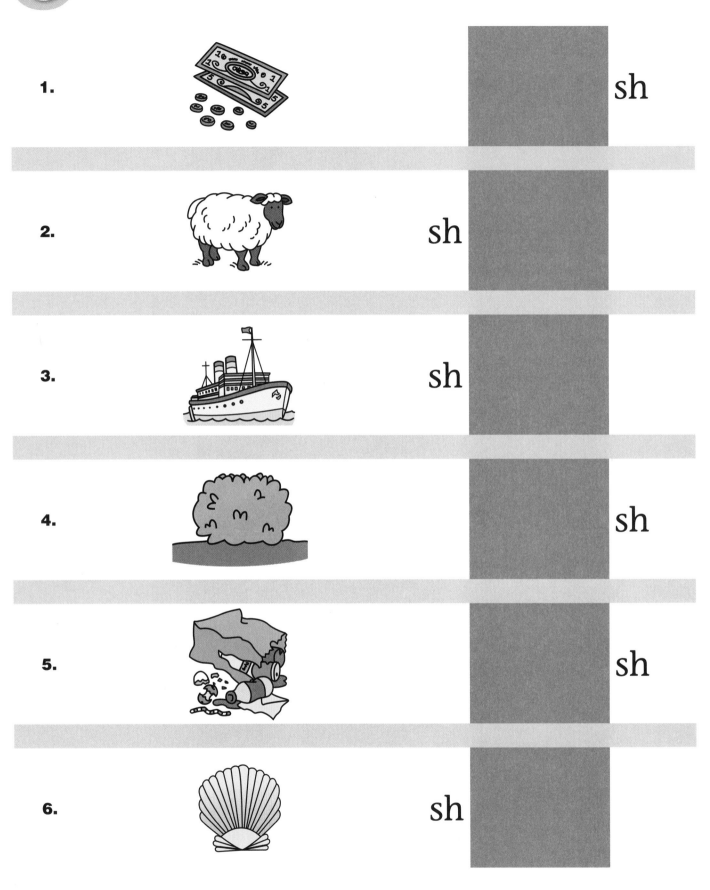

1.

sh

2.

sh

3.

sh

4.

sh

5.

sh

6.

sh

Phonics Intervention Centers
Consonant Digraphs and Blends

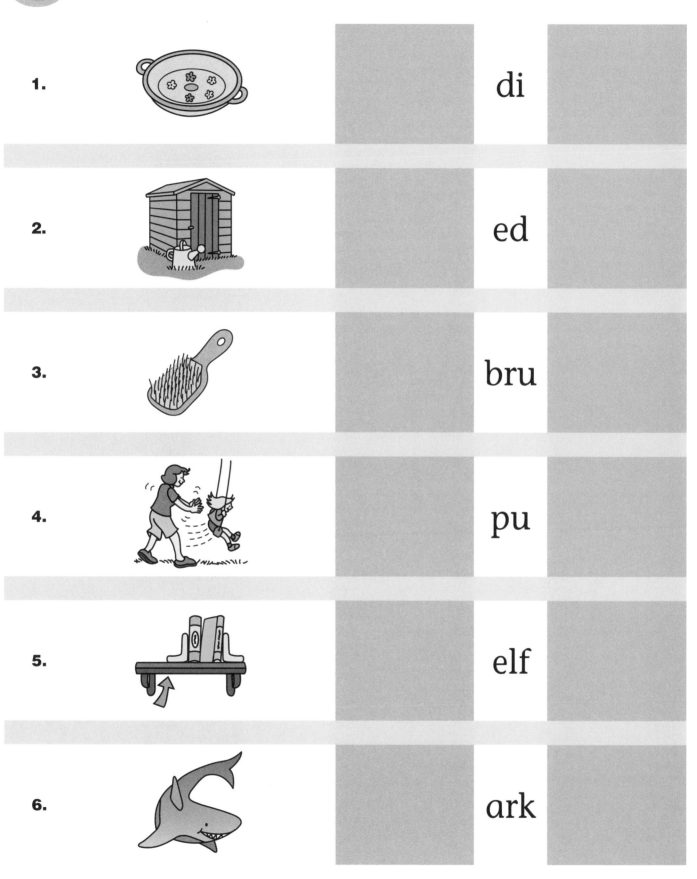

1.   di

2.   ed

3.   bru

4.   pu

5.   elf

6.   ark

1.

sh

2. sh

3. sh

4. sh

5. sh

6. sh

Phonics Intervention Centers
Consonant Digraphs and Blends

EMC 3522 • © Evan-Moor Corp.

Student 6	sh	sh	sh	sh	sh	sh
Student 5	sh	sh	sh	sh	sh	sh
Student 4	sh	sh	sh	sh	sh	sh
Student 3	sh	sh	sh	sh	sh	sh
Student 2	sh	sh	sh	sh	sh	sh
Student 1	sh	sh	sh	sh	sh	sh

Student 6 — EMC 3522 — Center 1 • Mat A
Student 6 — EMC 3522 — Center 1 • Mat A
Student 6 — EMC 3522 — Center 1 • Mat A
Student 6 — EMC 3522 — Center 1 • Mat A
Student 6 — EMC 3522 — Center 1 • Mat A
Student 6 — EMC 3522 — Center 1 • Mat A

Student 5 — EMC 3522 — Center 1 • Mat A
Student 5 — EMC 3522 — Center 1 • Mat A
Student 5 — EMC 3522 — Center 1 • Mat A
Student 5 — EMC 3522 — Center 1 • Mat A
Student 5 — EMC 3522 — Center 1 • Mat A
Student 5 — EMC 3522 — Center 1 • Mat A

Student 4 — EMC 3522 — Center 1 • Mat A
Student 4 — EMC 3522 — Center 1 • Mat A
Student 4 — EMC 3522 — Center 1 • Mat A
Student 4 — EMC 3522 — Center 1 • Mat A
Student 4 — EMC 3522 — Center 1 • Mat A
Student 4 — EMC 3522 — Center 1 • Mat A

Student 3 — EMC 3522 — Center 1 • Mat A
Student 3 — EMC 3522 — Center 1 • Mat A
Student 3 — EMC 3522 — Center 1 • Mat A
Student 3 — EMC 3522 — Center 1 • Mat A
Student 3 — EMC 3522 — Center 1 • Mat A
Student 3 — EMC 3522 — Center 1 • Mat A

Student 2 — EMC 3522 — Center 1 • Mat A
Student 2 — EMC 3522 — Center 1 • Mat A
Student 2 — EMC 3522 — Center 1 • Mat A
Student 2 — EMC 3522 — Center 1 • Mat A
Student 2 — EMC 3522 — Center 1 • Mat A
Student 2 — EMC 3522 — Center 1 • Mat A

Student 1 — EMC 3522 — Center 1 • Mat A
Student 1 — EMC 3522 — Center 1 • Mat A
Student 1 — EMC 3522 — Center 1 • Mat A
Student 1 — EMC 3522 — Center 1 • Mat A
Student 1 — EMC 3522 — Center 1 • Mat A
Student 1 — EMC 3522 — Center 1 • Mat A

Student 6	Student 5	Student 4	Student 3	Student 2	Student 1
bu	bu	bu	bu	bu	bu
ca	ca	ca	ca	ca	ca
eep	eep	eep	eep	eep	eep
ell	ell	ell	ell	ell	ell
ip	ip	ip	ip	ip	ip
tra	tra	tra	tra	tra	tra

Student 6 — EMC 3522 — Center 1 • Mat B

Student 6 — EMC 3522 — Center 1 • Mat B

Student 6 — EMC 3522 — Center 1 • Mat B

Student 6 — EMC 3522 — Center 1 • Mat B

Student 6 — EMC 3522 — Center 1 • Mat B

Student 6 — EMC 3522 — Center 1 • Mat B

Student 5 — EMC 3522 — Center 1 • Mat B

Student 5 — EMC 3522 — Center 1 • Mat B

Student 5 — EMC 3522 — Center 1 • Mat B

Student 5 — EMC 3522 — Center 1 • Mat B

Student 5 — EMC 3522 — Center 1 • Mat B

Student 5 — EMC 3522 — Center 1 • Mat B

Student 4 — EMC 3522 — Center 1 • Mat B

Student 4 — EMC 3522 — Center 1 • Mat B

Student 4 — EMC 3522 — Center 1 • Mat B

Student 4 — EMC 3522 — Center 1 • Mat B

Student 4 — EMC 3522 — Center 1 • Mat B

Student 4 — EMC 3522 — Center 1 • Mat B

Student 3 — EMC 3522 — Center 1 • Mat B

Student 3 — EMC 3522 — Center 1 • Mat B

Student 3 — EMC 3522 — Center 1 • Mat B

Student 3 — EMC 3522 — Center 1 • Mat B

Student 3 — EMC 3522 — Center 1 • Mat B

Student 3 — EMC 3522 — Center 1 • Mat B

Student 2 — EMC 3522 — Center 1 • Mat B

Student 2 — EMC 3522 — Center 1 • Mat B

Student 2 — EMC 3522 — Center 1 • Mat B

Student 2 — EMC 3522 — Center 1 • Mat B

Student 2 — EMC 3522 — Center 1 • Mat B

Student 2 — EMC 3522 — Center 1 • Mat B

Student 1 — EMC 3522 — Center 1 • Mat B

Student 1 — EMC 3522 — Center 1 • Mat B

Student 1 — EMC 3522 — Center 1 • Mat B

Student 1 — EMC 3522 — Center 1 • Mat B

Student 1 — EMC 3522 — Center 1 • Mat B

Student 1 — EMC 3522 — Center 1 • Mat B

Practice It!

Say the word that names the picture.
Fill in the first circle if you hear **/sh/** at the **beginning** of the word.
Fill in the second circle if you hear **/sh/** at the **end** of the word.

1.

sh
○────────○

2.

sh
○────────○

3.

sh
○────────○

4.

sh
○────────○

5.

sh
○────────○

6.

sh
○────────○

7.

sh
○────────○

8.

sh
○────────○

9.

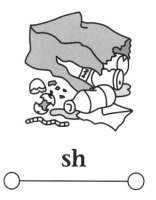

sh
○────────○

Read It!

Write the word on the line that best completes the sentence.

1. I will _____ my dish.
   wash   wish

2. I need cash to _____.
   ship   shop

3. She had to _____ to get the bus.
   rash   rush

4. A clam lives in a _____.
   shell   shed

5. Trish likes to _____ in the pool.
   splash   smash

6. I hit my _____ on the trash can.
   shine   shin

7. Shane needs a _____ to paint the shelf.
   brush   bush

8. My bed _____ has _____ on it.
   sheet   sheep   sheet   sheep

center

2

Consonant Digraph ch

For the Teacher

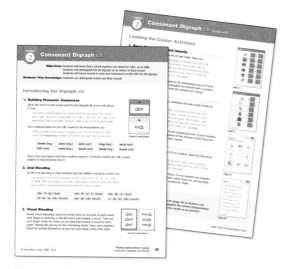

Lesson Plan

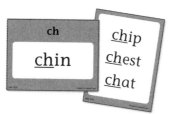
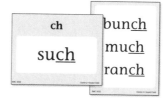

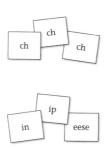

Sound Cards

Answer Keys

For the Student

front (Mat A)

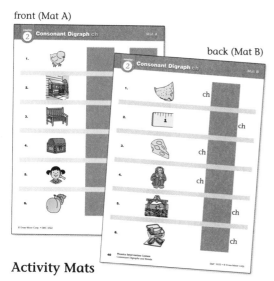

back (Mat B)

Activity Mats

ch

ch

ch

in   ip   eese

Task Cards

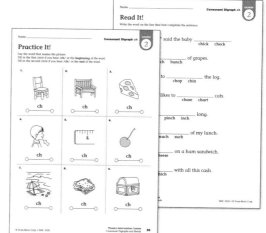

Practice and Assessment Activities

Consonant Digraph ch

Objectives: Students will learn that *c* and *h* together can stand for /ch/, as in **chin**.
Students will distinguish the *ch* digraph as an initial or final sound.
Students will blend sounds to read and understand words with the *ch* digraph.

Students' Prior Knowledge: Students can distinguish initial and final sounds.

Introducing the Digraph *ch*

1. Building Phonemic Awareness

Show the front of each sound card for the digraph *ch* as you talk about it. Say:

*The letters **c** and **h** together in a word stand for one sound. The sound is often /ch/. Repeat the sound after me: /ch/. (/ch/) You hear /ch/ at the beginning of the word **chin**. You hear /ch/ at the end of the word **such**.*

Have students listen for the /ch/ sound in the words below. Say:

*Listen carefully to the words I'm going to say. Each word has the /ch/ sound. Say **beginning** or **end** to tell where you hear /ch/ in the word.*

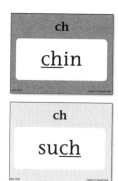

Sound Cards (front)

cheese (beg.)	**chew** (beg.)	**inch** (end)	**chop** (beg.)	**each** (end)
rich (end)	**chair** (beg.)	**lunch** (end)	**cheap** (beg.)	**touch** (end)

Read each word again and have students repeat it. If needed, stretch the /ch/ sound slightly to help students hear it.

2. Oral Blending

Model oral blending to help students hear the distinct sounds in a word. Say:

*I am going to say a word, sound by sound. Listen: /ch/ /ĭ/ /k/. The word is **chick**. Now I am going to say some other words, sound by sound. You blend the sounds for each word and tell me what the word is. Listen:*

/ch/ /ĭ/ /p/ (chip)	/ch/ /ĕ/ /s/ /t/ (chest)	/ch/ /ă/ /t/ (chat)
/b/ /ŭ/ /n/ /ch/ (bunch)	/m/ /ŭ/ /ch/ (much)	/r/ /ă/ /n/ /ch/ (ranch)

3. Visual Blending

Model visual blending, using the words listed on the back of each sound card. Begin by pointing to the first word and reading it aloud. Then run your finger under the letters as you blend the sounds to read the word again. Repeat this process for the remaining words. Next, have students blend the sounds themselves as you run your finger under each letter.

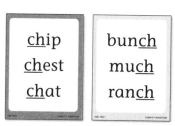

Sound Cards (back)

Leading the Center Activities

1. Read, Discriminate, and Identify ....

Give each student Mat A and a set of task cards. Then say:

*We're going to form words that begin or end with the letters **c-h**. Look at the picture in row 1. It is a chick. Do you hear /**ch**/ at the beginning of the word **chick** or at the end? (beginning) Place a card in the box in front of the letters **i-c-k**. Now let's blend the sounds and read the word: /**ch**/ /ĭ/ /k/ **chick**.*

Repeat this process with the pictures in the remaining rows, or if your students are capable, have them complete the activity with a partner. Give help when needed. Then go over the answers as a group.

2. Read and Understand ....

Have students turn over their mats. Distribute the task cards for Mat B. Then say:

*We're going to form words that name the pictures on this mat. Each word begins or ends with the /**ch**/ sound. Look at the picture in row 1. It is a chip. Now look at the letters on your cards. Which letters spell the ending of the word **chip**? (i-p) Place the **i-p** card in the box. Now let's blend the sounds and read the word: /**ch**/ /ĭ/ /p/ **chip**.*

Repeat this process with the pictures in the remaining rows. If your students are capable, have them tell you the names of the pictures rather than you saying them. (inch, cheese, chimp, ranch, lunch)

3. Practice the Skill ....

Distribute the Practice It! activity (page 55) to students. Read the directions aloud. Then say:

*Look at the first picture. It is a chair. Do you hear /**ch**/ at the beginning of the word **chair** or at the end? (beginning) Fill in the first circle to show that the letters **c-h** are at the beginning of the word.*

Repeat this process for the remaining pictures. If your students are capable, have them tell you the names of the pictures rather than you saying them. (bench, cheese, chin, inch, cherry, beach, sandwich, chest)

Apply and Assess

After the lesson, distribute the Read It! activity (page 56) to students and read the directions aloud. Have students complete the activity independently. Then listen to them read the sentences. Use the results as an informal assessment of students' skill mastery.

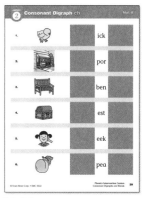
Mat A

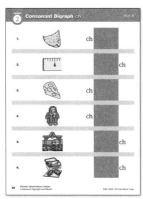
Mat B

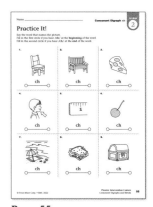
Page 55

Page 56

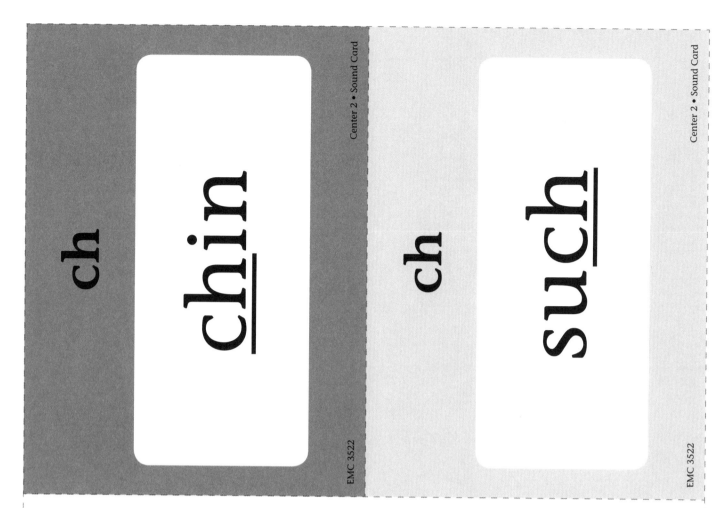

Answer Keys

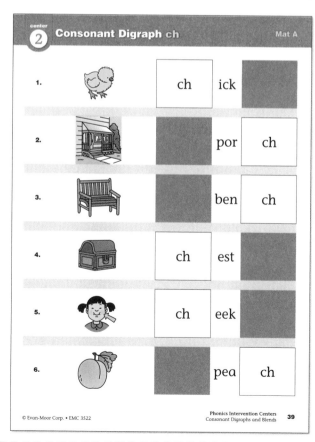

center 2 **Consonant Digraph ch** — Mat A

1. ch / ick
2. por / ch
3. ben / ch
4. ch / est
5. ch / eek
6. pea / ch

© Evan-Moor Corp. • EMC 3522

Phonics Intervention Centers
Consonant Digraphs and Blends **39**

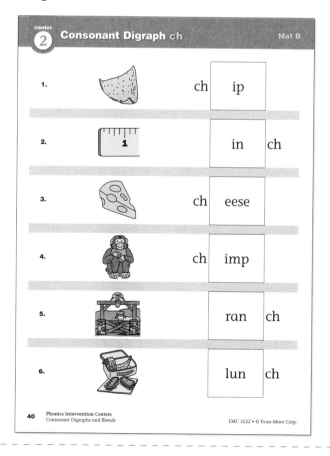

center 2 **Consonant Digraph ch** — Mat B

1. ch / ip
2. in / ch
3. ch / eese
4. ch / imp
5. ran / ch
6. lun / ch

40 Phonics Intervention Centers
Consonant Digraphs and Blends

EMC 3522 • © Evan-Moor Corp.

bunch

mu<u>ch</u>

ran<u>ch</u>

Center 2 • Sound Card

<u>ch</u>ip

<u>ch</u>est

<u>ch</u>at

Center 2 • Sound Card

Answer Keys

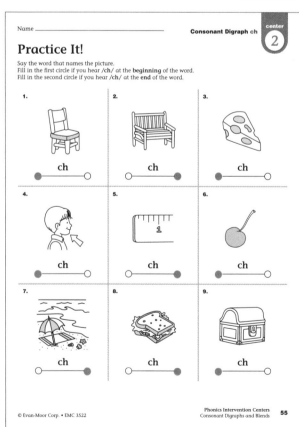

Name _____

Consonant Digraph ch

center **2**

Practice It!

Say the word that names the picture.
Fill in the first circle if you hear /ch/ at the **beginning** of the word.
Fill in the second circle if you hear /ch/ at the **end** of the word.

1. ch ● ○
2. ch ○ ●
3. ch ● ○
4. ch ● ○
5. ch ○ ●
6. ch ● ○
7. ch ○ ●
8. ch ○ ●
9. ch ● ○

© Evan-Moor Corp. • EMC 3522

Phonics Intervention Centers
Consonant Digraphs and Blends **55**

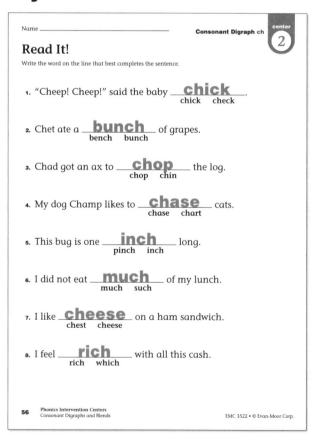

Name _____

Consonant Digraph ch

center **2**

Read It!

Write the word on the line that best completes the sentence.

1. "Cheep! Cheep!" said the baby **chick** .
   chick   check

2. Chet ate a **bunch** of grapes.
   bench   bunch

3. Chad got an ax to **chop** the log.
   chop   chin

4. My dog Champ likes to **chase** cats.
   chase   chart

5. This bug is one **inch** long.
   pinch   inch

6. I did not eat **much** of my lunch.
   much   such

7. I like **cheese** on a ham sandwich.
   chest   cheese

8. I feel **rich** with all this cash.
   rich   which

56 Phonics Intervention Centers
Consonant Digraphs and Blends

EMC 3522 • © Evan-Moor Corp.

1.   ick

2.   por

3.   ben

4.   est

5.   eek

6.   pea

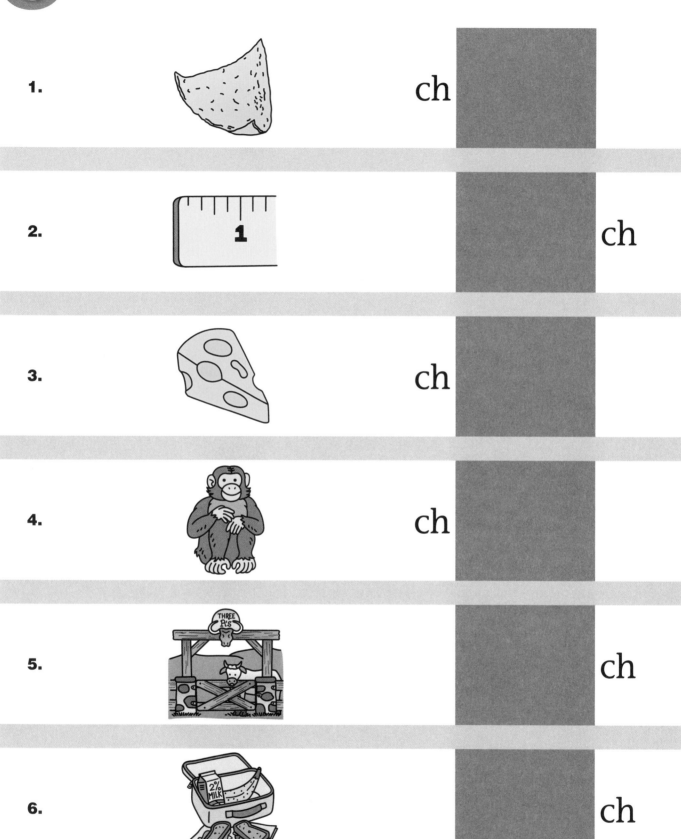

1.

           ch

2.

                  ch

3.

           ch

4.

           ch

5.

                  ch

6.

                  ch

1.

ick

2.

por

3.

ben

4.

est

5.

eek

6.

pea

1.  ch

2.  ch

3.  ch

4.  ch

5.  ch

6.  ch

1.   ick

2.   por

3.   ben

4.   est

5.   eek

6.   pea

1.  ch

2.  ch

3.  ch

4.  ch

5.  ch

6.  ch

Phonics Intervention Centers
Consonant Digraphs and Blends

EMC 3522 • © Evan-Moor Corp.

1. ick

2. por

3. ben

4. est

5. eek

6. pea

1.    ch

2.    ch

3.    ch

4.    ch

5.    ch

6.    ch

1. ick

2. por

3. ben

4. est

5. eek

6. pea

1.  ch

2.  ch

3.  ch

4.  ch

5.  ch

6.  ch

1. ick

2. por

3. ben

4. est

5. eek

6. pea

1.  ch

2.  ch

3.  ch

4.  ch

5.  ch

6.  ch

Student 6	ch	ch	ch	ch	ch	ch
Student 5	ch	ch	ch	ch	ch	ch
Student 4	ch	ch	ch	ch	ch	ch
Student 3	ch	ch	ch	ch	ch	ch
Student 2	ch	ch	ch	ch	ch	ch
Student 1	ch	ch	ch	ch	ch	ch

Student 6
EMC 3522
Center 2 • Mat A

Student 6
EMC 3522
Center 2 • Mat A

Student 6
EMC 3522
Center 2 • Mat A

Student 6
EMC 3522
Center 2 • Mat A

Student 6
EMC 3522
Center 2 • Mat A

Student 6
EMC 3522
Center 2 • Mat A

Student 5
EMC 3522
Center 2 • Mat A

Student 5
EMC 3522
Center 2 • Mat A

Student 5
EMC 3522
Center 2 • Mat A

Student 5
EMC 3522
Center 2 • Mat A

Student 5
EMC 3522
Center 2 • Mat A

Student 5
EMC 3522
Center 2 • Mat A

Student 4
EMC 3522
Center 2 • Mat A

Student 4
EMC 3522
Center 2 • Mat A

Student 4
EMC 3522
Center 2 • Mat A

Student 4
EMC 3522
Center 2 • Mat A

Student 4
EMC 3522
Center 2 • Mat A

Student 4
EMC 3522
Center 2 • Mat A

Student 3
EMC 3522
Center 2 • Mat A

Student 3
EMC 3522
Center 2 • Mat A

Student 3
EMC 3522
Center 2 • Mat A

Student 3
EMC 3522
Center 2 • Mat A

Student 3
EMC 3522
Center 2 • Mat A

Student 3
EMC 3522
Center 2 • Mat A

Student 2
EMC 3522
Center 2 • Mat A

Student 2
EMC 3522
Center 2 • Mat A

Student 2
EMC 3522
Center 2 • Mat A

Student 2
EMC 3522
Center 2 • Mat A

Student 2
EMC 3522
Center 2 • Mat A

Student 2
EMC 3522
Center 2 • Mat A

Student 1
EMC 3522
Center 2 • Mat A

Student 1
EMC 3522
Center 2 • Mat A

Student 1
EMC 3522
Center 2 • Mat A

Student 1
EMC 3522
Center 2 • Mat A

Student 1
EMC 3522
Center 2 • Mat A

Student 1
EMC 3522
Center 2 • Mat A

Student 6	ip	in	eese	imp	ran	lun
Student 5	ip	in	eese	imp	ran	lun
Student 4	ip	in	eese	imp	ran	lun
Student 3	ip	in	eese	imp	ran	lun
Student 2	ip	in	eese	imp	ran	lun
Student 1	ip	in	eese	imp	ran	lun

Student 6

EMC 3522
Center 2 • Mat B

Student 6

EMC 3522
Center 2 • Mat B

Student 6

EMC 3522
Center 2 • Mat B

Student 6

EMC 3522
Center 2 • Mat B

Student 6

EMC 3522
Center 2 • Mat B

Student 6

EMC 3522
Center 2 • Mat B

Student 5

EMC 3522
Center 2 • Mat B

Student 5

EMC 3522
Center 2 • Mat B

Student 5

EMC 3522
Center 2 • Mat B

Student 5

EMC 3522
Center 2 • Mat B

Student 5

EMC 3522
Center 2 • Mat B

Student 5

EMC 3522
Center 2 • Mat B

Student 4

EMC 3522
Center 2 • Mat B

Student 4

EMC 3522
Center 2 • Mat B

Student 4

EMC 3522
Center 2 • Mat B

Student 4

EMC 3522
Center 2 • Mat B

Student 4

EMC 3522
Center 2 • Mat B

Student 4

EMC 3522
Center 2 • Mat B

Student 3

EMC 3522
Center 2 • Mat B

Student 3

EMC 3522
Center 2 • Mat B

Student 3

EMC 3522
Center 2 • Mat B

Student 3

EMC 3522
Center 2 • Mat B

Student 3

EMC 3522
Center 2 • Mat B

Student 3

EMC 3522
Center 2 • Mat B

Student 2

EMC 3522
Center 2 • Mat B

Student 2

EMC 3522
Center 2 • Mat B

Student 2

EMC 3522
Center 2 • Mat B

Student 2

EMC 3522
Center 2 • Mat B

Student 2

EMC 3522
Center 2 • Mat B

Student 2

EMC 3522
Center 2 • Mat B

Student 1

EMC 3522
Center 2 • Mat B

Student 1

EMC 3522
Center 2 • Mat B

Student 1

EMC 3522
Center 2 • Mat B

Student 1

EMC 3522
Center 2 • Mat B

Student 1

EMC 3522
Center 2 • Mat B

Student 1

EMC 3522
Center 2 • Mat B

Practice It!

Say the word that names the picture.
Fill in the first circle if you hear **/ch/** at the **beginning** of the word.
Fill in the second circle if you hear **/ch/** at the **end** of the word.

1.

ch
○———○

2.

ch
○———○

3.

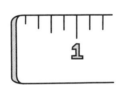

ch
○———○

4.

ch
○———○

5.

ch
○———○

6.

ch
○———○

7.

ch
○———○

8.

ch
○———○

9.

ch
○———○

Read It!

Write the word on the line that best completes the sentence.

1. "Cheep! Cheep!" said the baby _____.
   chick   check

2. Chet ate a _____ of grapes.
   bench   bunch

3. Chad got an ax to _____ the log.
   chop   chin

4. My dog Champ likes to _____ cats.
   chase   chart

5. This bug is one _____ long.
   pinch   inch

6. I did not eat _____ of my lunch.
   much   such

7. I like _____ on a ham sandwich.
   chest   cheese

8. I feel _____ with all this cash.
   rich   which

center 3

Consonant Digraph th

For the Teacher

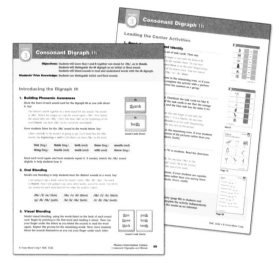

Lesson Plan

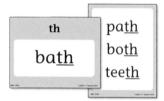

Sound Cards

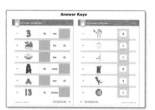

Answer Keys

For the Student

front (Mat A)

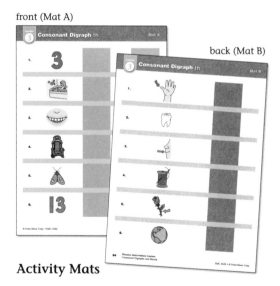

back (Mat B)

Activity Mats

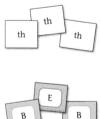

Task Cards

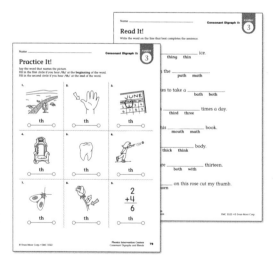

Practice and Assessment Activities

Consonant Digraph th

Objectives: Students will learn that *t* and *h* together can stand for /th/, as in **thank**.
Students will distinguish the *th* digraph as an initial or final sound.
Students will blend sounds to read and understand words with the *th* digraph.

Students' Prior Knowledge: Students can distinguish initial and final sounds.

Introducing the Digraph *th*

1. Building Phonemic Awareness

Show the front of each sound card for the digraph *th* as you talk about it. Say:

*The letters **t** and **h** together in a word stand for one sound. The sound is /th/. Watch my tongue as I say the sound again: /th/. Now repeat the sound after me: /th/. (/th/) You hear /th/ at the beginning of the word **thank**. You hear /th/ at the end of the word **bath**.*

Have students listen for the /th/ sound in the words below. Say:

*Listen carefully to the words I'm going to say. Each word has the /th/ sound. Say **beginning** or **end** to tell where you hear /th/ in the word.*

Sound Cards (front)

thin (beg.)	**think** (beg.)	**both** (end)	**three** (beg.)	**mouth** (end)
thing (beg.)	**fourth** (end)	**tooth** (end)	**with** (end)	**throw** (beg.)

Read each word again and have students repeat it. If needed, stretch the /th/ sound slightly to help students hear it.

2. Oral Blending

Model oral blending to help students hear the distinct sounds in a word. Say:

*I am going to say a word, sound by sound. Listen: /th/ /ŭ/ /m/. The word is **thumb**. Now I am going to say some other words, sound by sound. You blend the sounds for each word and tell me what the word is. Listen:*

/th/ /ĭ/ /n/ (thin)	/th/ /r/ /ē/ (three)	/th/ /ĭ/ /k/ (thick)
/p/ /ă/ /th/ (path)	/b/ /ō/ /th/ (both)	/t/ /ē/ /th/ (teeth)

3. Visual Blending

Model visual blending, using the words listed on the back of each sound card. Begin by pointing to the first word and reading it aloud. Then run your finger under the letters as you blend the sounds to read the word again. Repeat this process for the remaining words. Next, have students blend the sounds themselves as you run your finger under each letter.

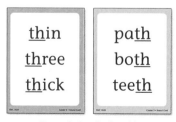

Sound Cards (back)

Leading the Center Activities

1. Read, Discriminate, and Identify ....

Give each student Mat A and a set of task cards. Then say:

*We're going to form words that begin or end with the letters **t-h**. Look at the picture in row 1. It is the number three. Do you hear /th/ at the beginning of the word **three** or at the end? (beginning) Place a card in the box in front of the letters **r-e-e**. Now let's blend the sounds and read the word: /th/ /r/ /ē/ **three**.*

Repeat this process with the pictures in the remaining rows, or if your students are capable, have them complete the activity with a partner. Give help when needed. Then go over the answers as a group.

2. Read and Understand ....

Have students turn over their mats. Distribute the task cards for Mat B. Tell students to look at both sides of the task cards to see that the orange side has the letter **B** for **beginning**, and the blue side has the letter **E** for **end**. Then say:

*The words that name the pictures on this mat begin or end with the /th/ sound. Look at the picture in row 1. It is a thumb. Do you hear /th/ at the beginning of the word **thumb** or at the end? (beginning) Place the letter **B** for **beginning** in the box next to the picture.*

Repeat this process with the pictures in the remaining rows. If your students are capable, have them tell you the names of the pictures rather than you saying them. (tooth, mouth, thread, thorn, Earth)

3. Practice the Skill ....

Distribute the Practice It! activity (page 79) to students. Read the directions aloud. Then say:

*Look at the first picture. It shows a path. Do you hear /th/ at the beginning of the word **path** or at the end? (end) Fill in the second circle to show that the letters **t-h** are at the end of the word.*

Repeat this process for the remaining pictures. If your students are capable, have them tell you the names of the pictures rather than you saying them. (thumb, Thursday, throne, tooth, throw, moth, thorn, math)

Apply and Assess

After the lesson, distribute the Read It! activity (page 80) to students and read the directions aloud. Have students complete the activity independently. Then listen to them read the sentences. Use the results as an informal assessment of students' skill mastery.

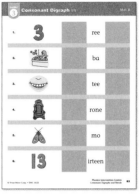

Mat A

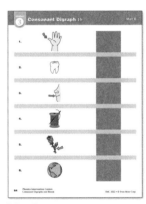

Mat B

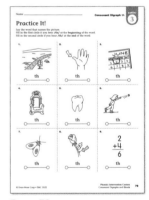

Page 79

Page 80

th

thank

th

bath

EMC 3522

EMC 3522

Answer Keys

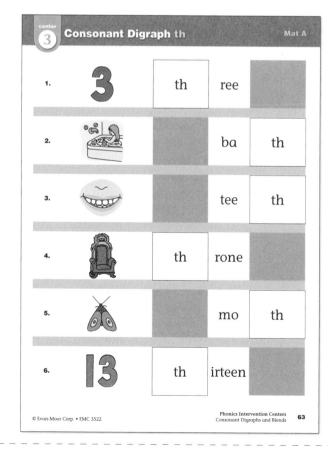

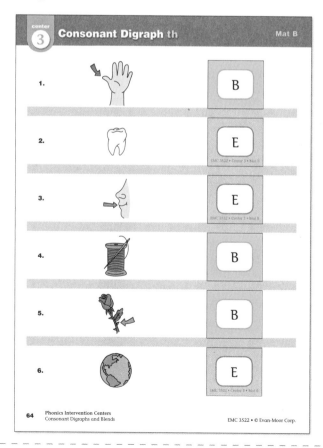

path

both

teeth

Center 3 • Sound Card

thin

three

thick

Center 3 • Sound Card

Answer Keys

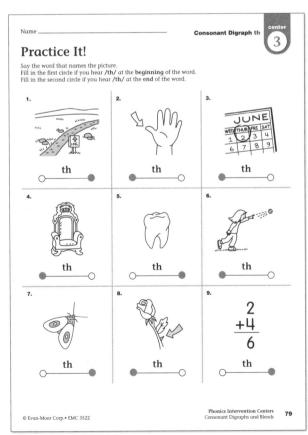

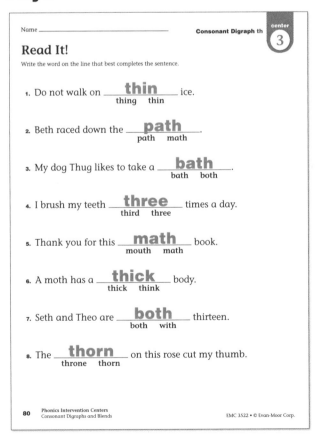

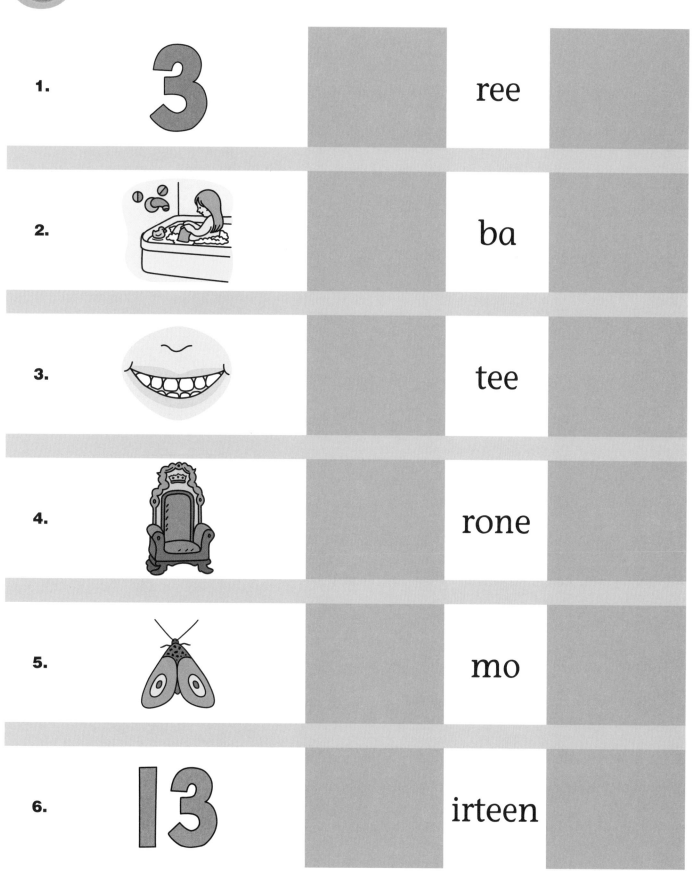

1. **3** ree

2. ba

3. tee

4. rone

5. mo

6. **13** irteen

Consonant Digraph th

1.

2.

3.

4.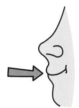

5.

6.

Phonics Intervention Centers
Consonant Digraphs and Blends

EMC 3522 • © Evan-Moor Corp.

1. **3**   ree

2.   ba

3.   tee

4.   rone

5.   mo

6. **13**   irteen

1.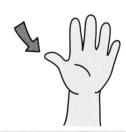

2.

3.

4.

5.

6.

Phonics Intervention Centers
Consonant Digraphs and Blends

EMC 3522 • © Evan-Moor Corp.

1.	3		ree	
2.			ba	
3.			tee	
4.			rone	
5.			mo	
6.	13		irteen	

1.

2.

3.

4.

5.

6.

Phonics Intervention Centers
Consonant Digraphs and Blends

EMC 3522 • © Evan-Moor Corp.

1. **3**   ree

2.   ba

3.   tee

4.   rone

5.   mo

6. **13**   irteen

1.

2.

3.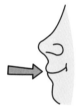

4.

5.

6.

Phonics Intervention Centers
Consonant Digraphs and Blends

EMC 3522 • © Evan-Moor Corp.

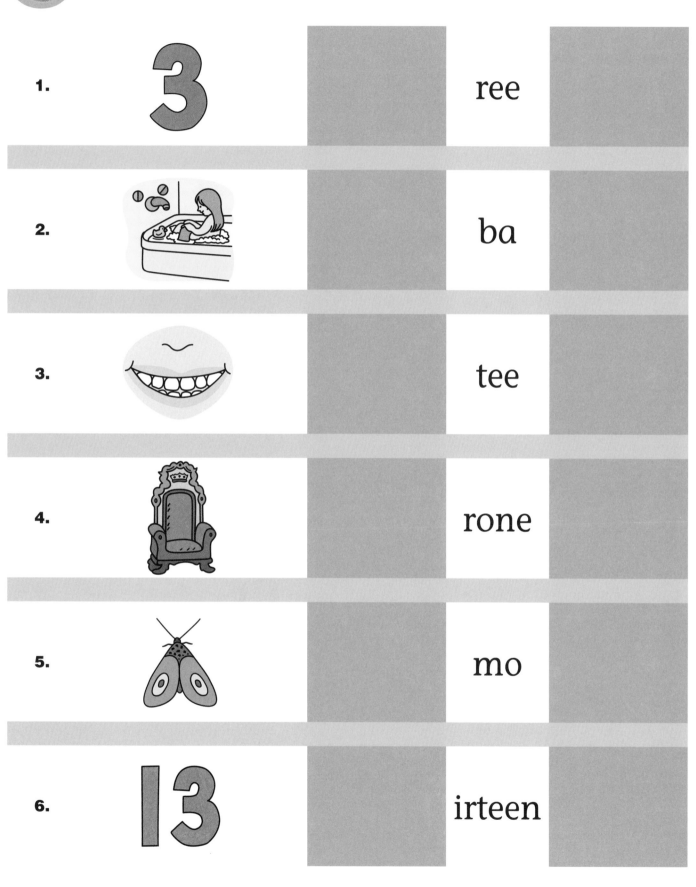

1. **3**   ree

2.   ba

3.   tee

4.   rone

5.   mo

6. **13**   irteen

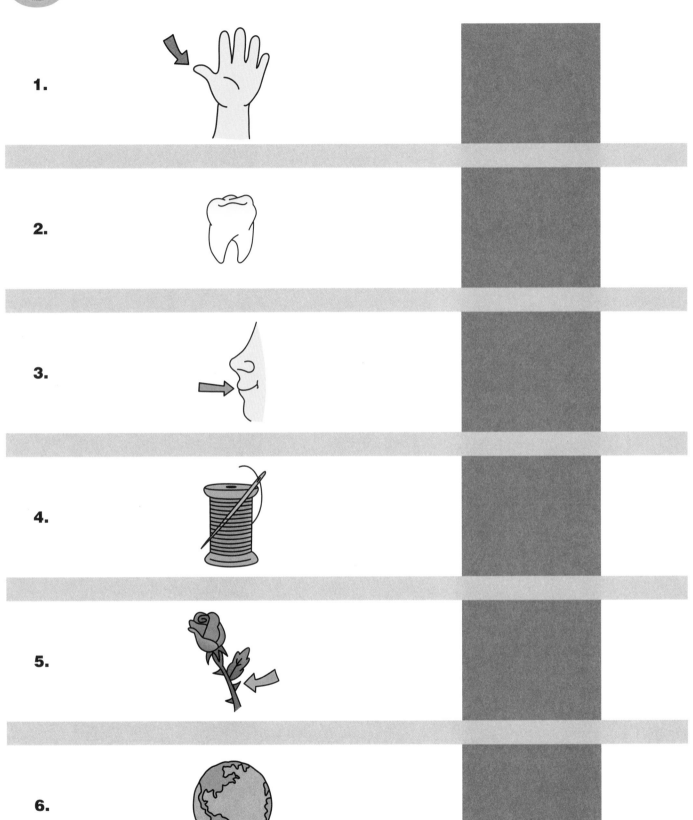

1.

2.

3.

4.

5.

6.

1. **3** ree

2. ba

3. tee

4. rone

5. mo

6. **13** irteen

1.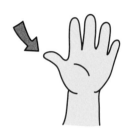

2.

3.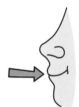

4.

5.

6.

Student 6 th	th	th	th	th	th
Student 5 th	th	th	th	th	th
Student 4 th	th	th	th	th	th
Student 3 th	th	th	th	th	th
Student 2 th	th	th	th	th	th
Student 1 th	th	th	th	th	th

Student 6 EMC 3522 Center 3 • Mat A	**Student 6** EMC 3522 Center 3 • Mat A	**Student 6** EMC 3522 Center 3 • Mat A	**Student 6** EMC 3522 Center 3 • Mat A	**Student 6** EMC 3522 Center 3 • Mat A	**Student 6** EMC 3522 Center 3 • Mat A	**Student 6** EMC 3522 Center 3 • Mat A	**Student 6** EMC 3522 Center 3 • Mat A	**Student 6** EMC 3522 Center 3 • Mat A	**Student 6** EMC 3522 Center 3 • Mat A
Student 5 EMC 3522 Center 3 • Mat A	**Student 5** EMC 3522 Center 3 • Mat A	**Student 5** EMC 3522 Center 3 • Mat A	**Student 5** EMC 3522 Center 3 • Mat A	**Student 5** EMC 3522 Center 3 • Mat A	**Student 5** EMC 3522 Center 3 • Mat A	**Student 5** EMC 3522 Center 3 • Mat A	**Student 5** EMC 3522 Center 3 • Mat A	**Student 5** EMC 3522 Center 3 • Mat A	**Student 5** EMC 3522 Center 3 • Mat A
Student 4 EMC 3522 Center 3 • Mat A	**Student 4** EMC 3522 Center 3 • Mat A	**Student 4** EMC 3522 Center 3 • Mat A	**Student 4** EMC 3522 Center 3 • Mat A	**Student 4** EMC 3522 Center 3 • Mat A	**Student 4** EMC 3522 Center 3 • Mat A	**Student 4** EMC 3522 Center 3 • Mat A	**Student 4** EMC 3522 Center 3 • Mat A	**Student 4** EMC 3522 Center 3 • Mat A	**Student 4** EMC 3522 Center 3 • Mat A
Student 3 EMC 3522 Center 3 • Mat A	**Student 3** EMC 3522 Center 3 • Mat A	**Student 3** EMC 3522 Center 3 • Mat A	**Student 3** EMC 3522 Center 3 • Mat A	**Student 3** EMC 3522 Center 3 • Mat A	**Student 3** EMC 3522 Center 3 • Mat A	**Student 3** EMC 3522 Center 3 • Mat A	**Student 3** EMC 3522 Center 3 • Mat A	**Student 3** EMC 3522 Center 3 • Mat A	**Student 3** EMC 3522 Center 3 • Mat A
Student 2 EMC 3522 Center 3 • Mat A	**Student 2** EMC 3522 Center 3 • Mat A	**Student 2** EMC 3522 Center 3 • Mat A	**Student 2** EMC 3522 Center 3 • Mat A	**Student 2** EMC 3522 Center 3 • Mat A	**Student 2** EMC 3522 Center 3 • Mat A	**Student 2** EMC 3522 Center 3 • Mat A	**Student 2** EMC 3522 Center 3 • Mat A	**Student 2** EMC 3522 Center 3 • Mat A	**Student 2** EMC 3522 Center 3 • Mat A
Student 1 EMC 3522 Center 3 • Mat A	**Student 1** EMC 3522 Center 3 • Mat A	**Student 1** EMC 3522 Center 3 • Mat A	**Student 1** EMC 3522 Center 3 • Mat A	**Student 1** EMC 3522 Center 3 • Mat A	**Student 1** EMC 3522 Center 3 • Mat A	**Student 1** EMC 3522 Center 3 • Mat A	**Student 1** EMC 3522 Center 3 • Mat A	**Student 1** EMC 3522 Center 3 • Mat A	**Student 1** EMC 3522 Center 3 • Mat A

Student 6

B B B B B B

Student 5

B B B B B B

Student 4

B B B B B B

Student 3

B B B B B B

Student 2

B B B B B B

Student 1

B B B B B B

Phonics Intervention Centers
Consonant Digraphs and Blends

EMC 3522 • © Evan-Moor Corp.

Practice It!

Say the word that names the picture.
Fill in the first circle if you hear **/th/** at the **beginning** of the word.
Fill in the second circle if you hear **/th/** at the **end** of the word.

1.

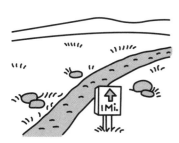

th
◯━━━━━◯

2.

th
◯━━━━━◯

3.

th
◯━━━━━◯

4.

th
◯━━━━━◯

5.

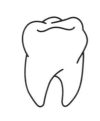

th
◯━━━━━◯

6.

th
◯━━━━━◯

7.

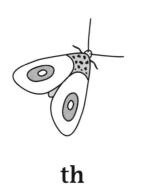

th
◯━━━━━◯

8.

th
◯━━━━━◯

9.

$$\begin{array}{r} 2 \\ +4 \\ \hline 6 \end{array}$$

th
◯━━━━━◯

Name _____

Read It!

Write the word on the line that best completes the sentence.

1. Do not walk on _____ ice.
   thing   thin

2. Beth raced down the _____.
   path   math

3. My dog Thug likes to take a _____.
   bath   both

4. I brush my teeth _____ times a day.
   third   three

5. Thank you for this _____ book.
   mouth   math

6. A moth has a _____ body.
   thick   think

7. Seth and Theo are _____ thirteen.
   both   with

8. The _____ on this rose cut my thumb.
   throne   thorn

center

4

Consonant Digraphs Review

For the Teacher

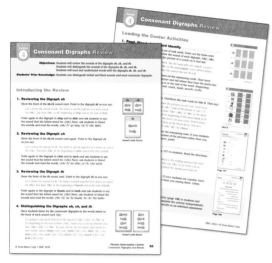

Lesson Plan

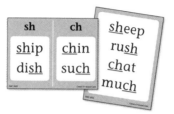

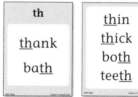

Sound Cards

Answer Keys

For the Student

front (Mat A)

back (Mat B)

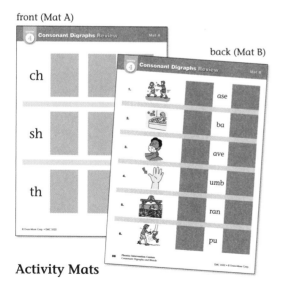

Activity Mats

Task Cards

Practice and Assessment Activities

Phonics Intervention Centers
Consonant Digraphs and Blends

EMC 3522 • © Evan-Moor Corp.

4

Consonant Digraphs Review

Objectives: Students will review the sounds of the digraphs *sh*, *ch*, and *th*.
Students will distinguish the sounds of the digraphs *sh*, *ch*, and *th*.
Students will read and understand words with the digraphs *sh*, *ch*, and *th*.

Students' Prior Knowledge: Students can distinguish initial and final sounds and read consonant digraphs.

Introducing the Review

1. Reviewing the Digraph *sh*

Show the front of the **sh/ch** sound card. Point to the digraph **sh** as you say:

Let's review the sound of s-h. The letters s and h together in a word stand for /sh/. You hear /sh/ at the beginning of ship and at the end of dish.

Point again to the digraph in **ship** and in **dish** and ask students to say the sound that the letters stand for. (/sh/) Next, ask students to blend the sounds and read the words. (/sh/ /ĭ/ /p/ ship; /d/ /ĭ/ /sh/ dish)

2. Reviewing the Digraph *ch*

Show the front of the **sh/ch** sound card again. Point to the digraph **ch** as you say:

Let's review the sound of c-h. The letters c and h together in a word can stand for /ch/. You hear /ch/ at the beginning of chin and at the end of such.

Point again to the digraph in **chin** and in **such** and ask students to say the sound that the letters stand for. (/ch/) Next, ask students to blend the sounds and read the words. (/ch/ /ĭ/ /n/ chin; /s/ /ŭ/ /ch/ such)

3. Reviewing the Digraph *th*

Show the front of the **th** sound card. Point to the digraph **th** as you say:

Let's review the sound of t-h. The letters t and h together in a word can stand for /th/. You hear /th/ at the beginning of thank and at the end of bath.

Point again to the digraph in **thank** and in **bath** and ask students to say the sound that the letters stand for. (/th/) Next, ask students to blend the sounds and read the words. (/th/ /ă/ /n/ /k/ thank; /b/ /ă/ /th/ bath)

4. Distinguishing the Digraphs *sh*, *ch*, and *th*

Have students listen for the consonant digraphs in the words listed on the back of each sound card. Say:

I'm going to say words that have the sound of /sh/, /ch/, or /th/ at the beginning or the end of them. First, I want you to tell me whether you hear /sh/, /ch/, or /th/. Second, tell me the two letters that stand for that sound. Listen: sheep (/sh/, s-h), teeth (/th/, t-h), thin (/th/, t-h), chat (/ch/, c-h), rush (/sh/, s-h), thick (/th/, t-h), much (/ch/, c-h), both (/th/, t-h).

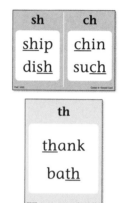
Sound Cards (front)

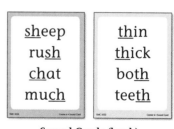
Sound Cards (back)

© Evan-Moor Corp. • EMC 3522

Phonics Intervention Centers
Consonant Digraphs and Blends
83

Leading the Center Activities

1. Read, Discriminate, and Identify

Give each student Mat A and a set of task cards. Point out the three rows of digraphs on the mat and review the sound of each digraph: **/ch/**, **/sh/**, **/th/**. Then show the card with the picture of a couch on it and say:

*The picture on this card is a couch. Say the word after me: **couch**. (couch) Do you hear /ch/, /sh/, or /th/ in the word **couch**? (/ch/) Which letters on the mat say /ch/? (c-h) Place the card in the row for **c-h**.*

Repeat this process with the pictures on the remaining cards. Then have students say the word for each picture and tell where they hear the particular digraph sound—at the beginning or at the end of the word. (beginning: chain, check, shark, shoe, thirty; end: couch, leash, mouth, tooth)

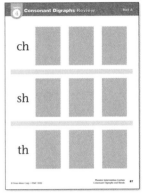

Mat A

2. Read and Understand

Have students turn over their mats. Distribute the task cards for Mat B. Then say:

*We're going to form words that name the pictures on this mat. Each word begins or ends with /ch/, /sh/, or /th/. Look at the picture in row 1. It shows a boy chasing a girl. Do you hear /ch/, /sh/, or /th/ in the word **chase**? (/ch/) Do you hear /ch/ at the beginning of the word **chase** or at the end? (beginning) Now look at the letters on your cards. Which letters say /ch/? (c-h) Place a **c-h** card in front of the letters **a-s-e**. Now let's blend the sounds and read the word: /ch/ /ā/ /s/ **chase**.*

Repeat this process with the pictures in the remaining rows. If your students are capable, have them tell you the names of the pictures rather than you saying them. (bath, shave, thumb, ranch, push)

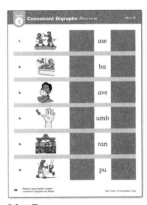

Mat B

3. Practice the Skill

Distribute the Practice It! activity (page 107) to students. Read the directions aloud. Then say:

*Look at the first picture. It is a bench. What is the ending sound in the word **bench**? (/ch/) Which two letters in the box say /ch/? (c-h) Write **c-h** on the line after the letters **b-e-n**. Now let's blend the sounds and read the word: /b/ /ě/ /n/ /ch/ **bench**.*

Repeat this process to complete the page. If your students are capable, have them say the names of the pictures rather than you saying them. (chest, fish, moth, shell, path, cheese, three)

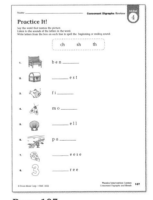

Page 107

Apply and Assess

After the lesson, distribute the Read It! activity (page 108) to students and read the directions aloud. Have students complete the activity independently. Then listen to them read the story. Use the results as an informal assessment of students' skill mastery.

Page 108

EMC 3522

ch

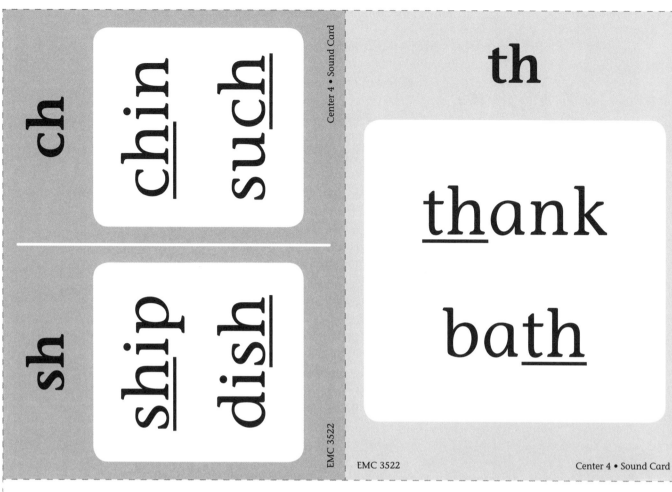

chin

such

ship

dish

Center 4 • Sound Card

th

thank

ba<u>th</u>

EMC 3522

Center 4 • Sound Card

sh

Answer Keys

Consonant Digraphs Review — Mat A

center 4

Cards may appear in any order within a section.

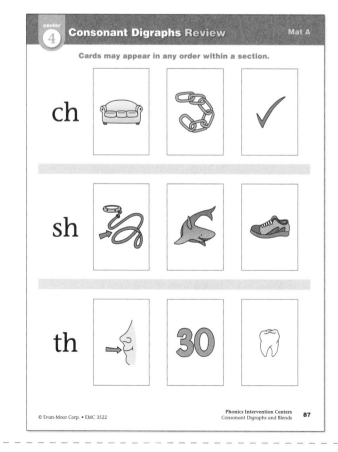

ch

sh

th

© Evan-Moor Corp. • EMC 3522

Phonics Intervention Centers
Consonant Digraphs and Blends

87

Consonant Digraphs Review — Mat B

center 4

1. ch ase

2. ba th

3. sh ave

4. th umb

5. ran ch

6. pu sh

88 Phonics Intervention Centers
Consonant Digraphs and Blends

EMC 3522 • © Evan-Moor Corp.

thin

thick

both

teeth

sheep

rush

chat

much

Answer Keys

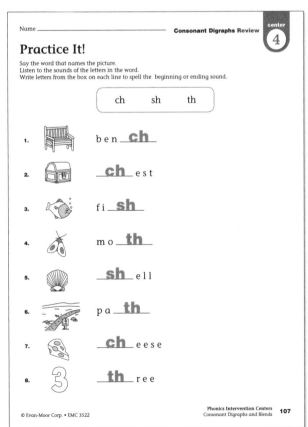

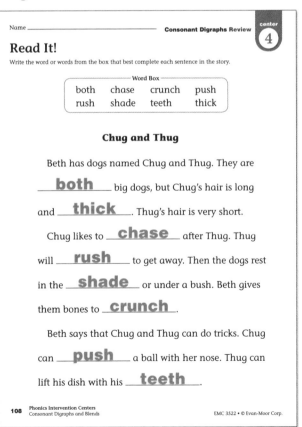

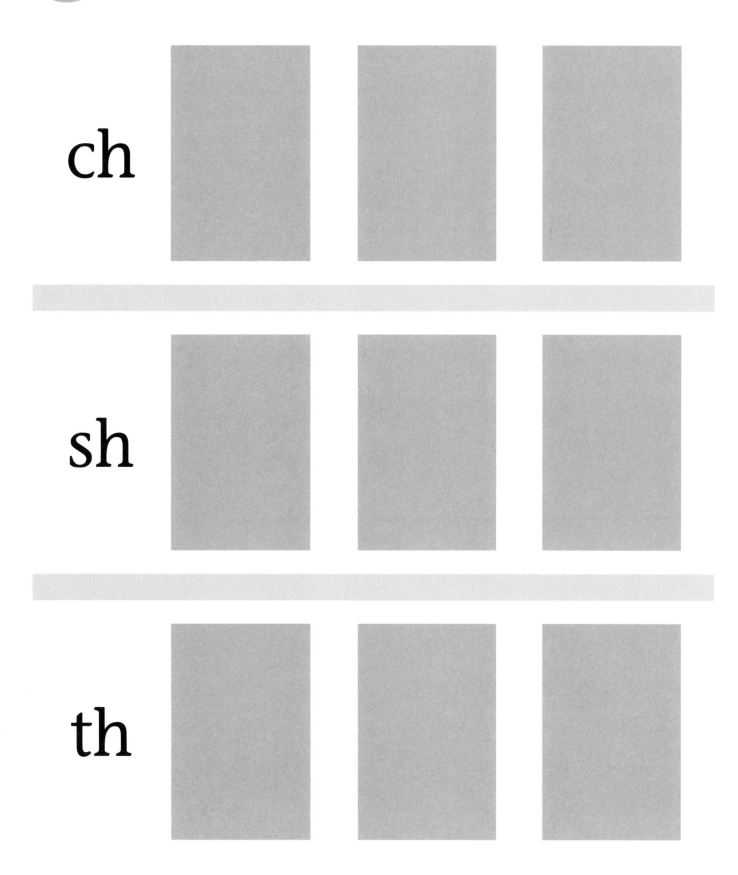

ch

sh

th

1. ase

2. ba

3. ave

4. umb

5. ran

6. pu

Phonics Intervention Centers
Consonant Digraphs and Blends

EMC 3522 • © Evan-Moor Corp.

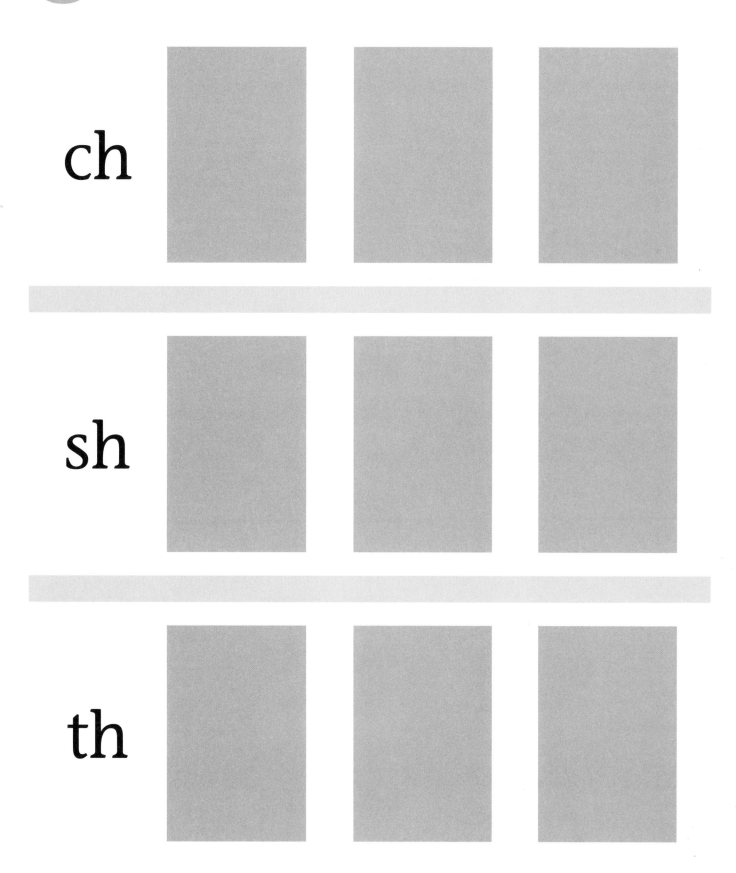

ch

sh

th

1.   ase

2.   ba

3.   ave

4.   umb

5.   ran

6.   pu

Phonics Intervention Centers
Consonant Digraphs and Blends

ch

sh

th

1. ase

2. ba

3. ave

4. umb

5. ran

6. pu

Phonics Intervention Centers
Consonant Digraphs and Blends

EMC 3522 • © Evan-Moor Corp.

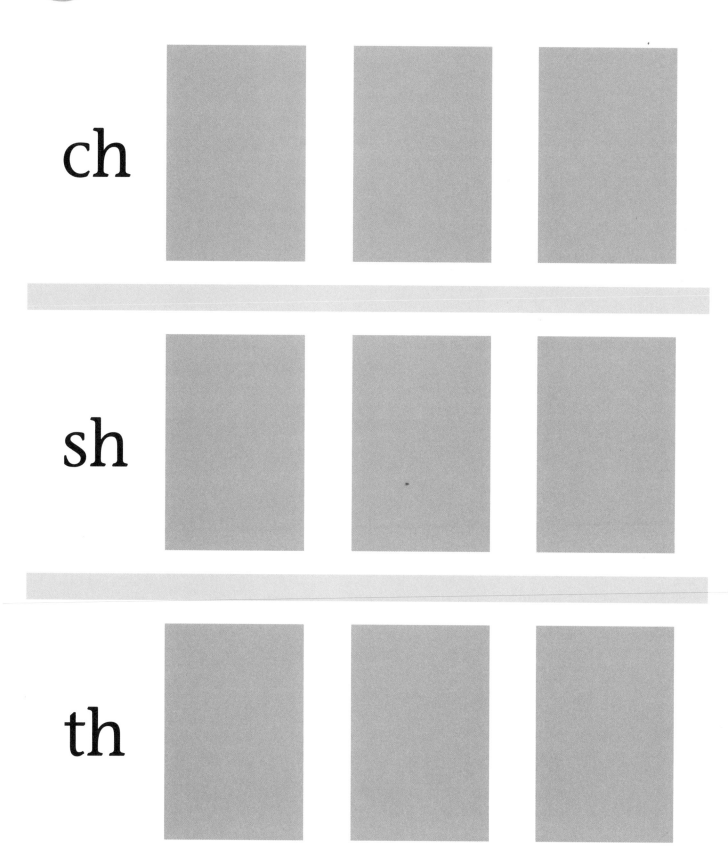

ch

sh

th

Consonant Digraphs Review

1. ase

2. ba

3. ave

4. umb

5. ran

6. pu

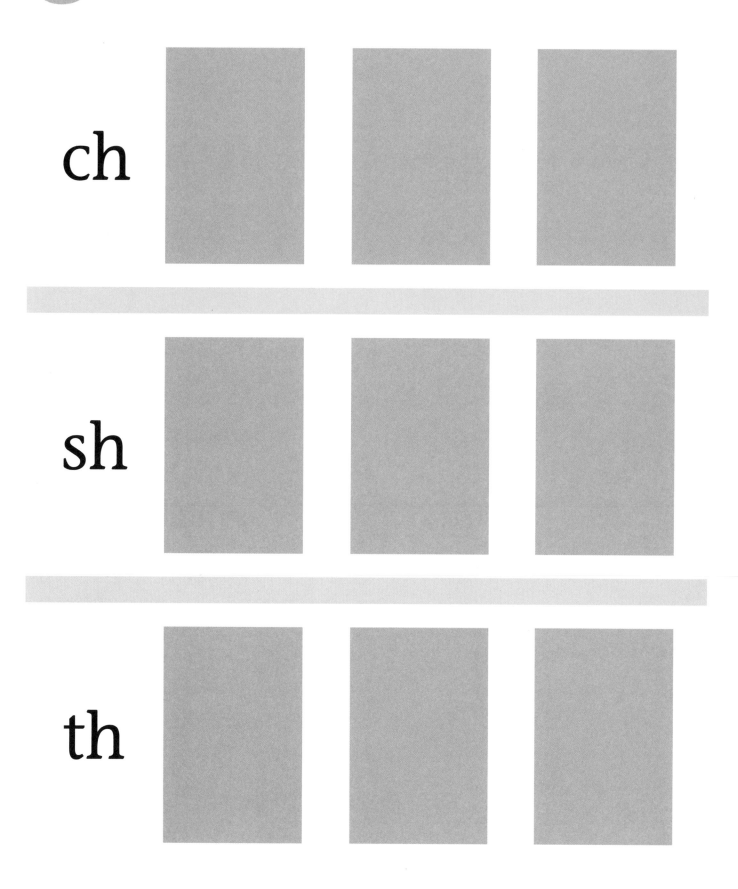

ch

sh

th

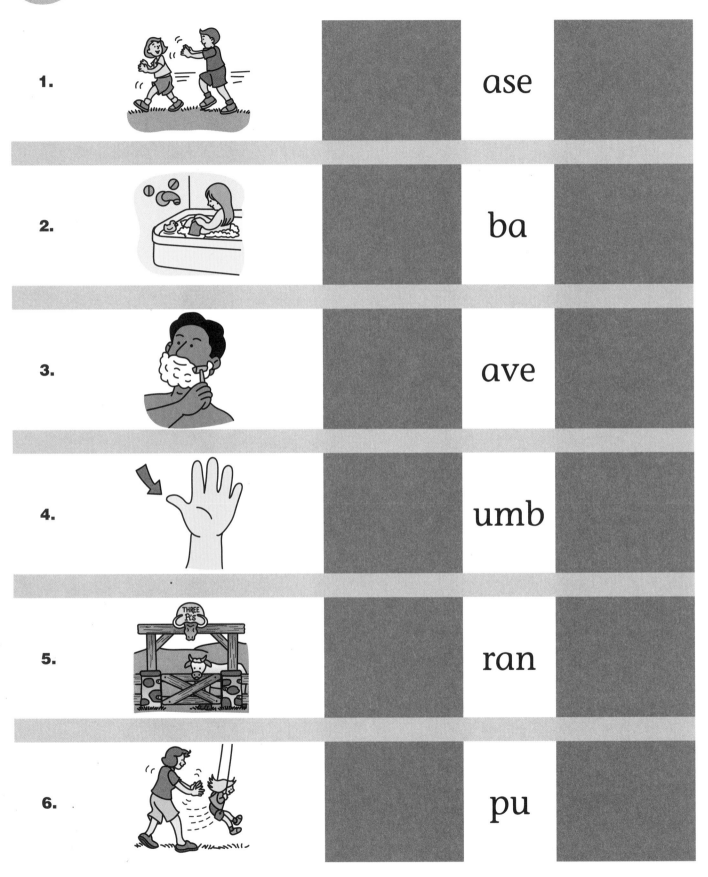

1. ase

2. ba

3. ave

4. umb

5. ran

6. pu

Phonics Intervention Centers
Consonant Digraphs and Blends

EMC 3522 • © Evan-Moor Corp.

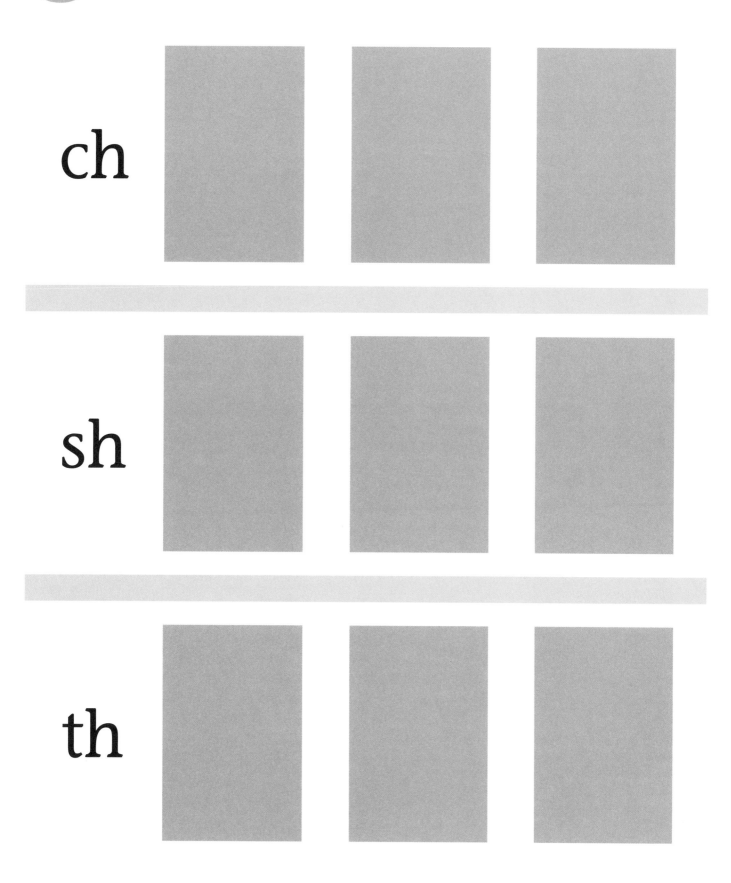

ch

sh

th

1.   ase

2.   ba

3.   ave

4.   umb

5.   ran

6.   pu

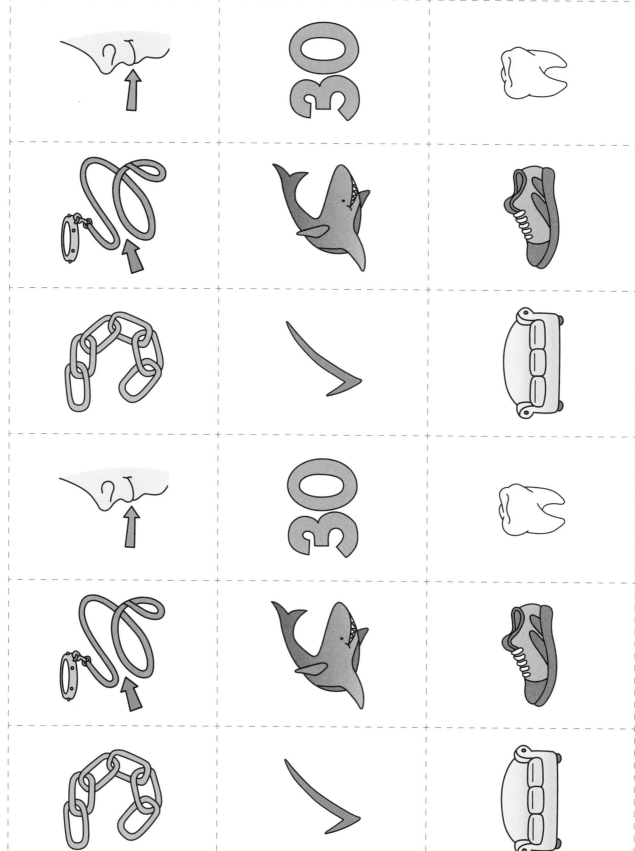

Task Cards

Student 2

EMC 3522
Center 4 • Mat A

Student 2

EMC 3522
Center 4 • Mat A

Student 2

EMC 3522
Center 4 • Mat A

Student 2

EMC 3522
Center 4 • Mat A

Student 2

EMC 3522
Center 4 • Mat A

Student 2

EMC 3522
Center 4 • Mat A

Student 1

EMC 3522
Center 4 • Mat A

Student 2

EMC 3522
Center 4 • Mat A

Student 1

EMC 3522
Center 4 • Mat A

Student 1

EMC 3522
Center 4 • Mat A

Student 1

EMC 3522
Center 4 • Mat A

Student 1

EMC 3522
Center 4 • Mat A

Student 1

EMC 3522
Center 4 • Mat A

Student 1

EMC 3522
Center 4 • Mat A

Student 4

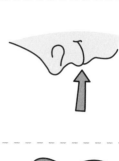

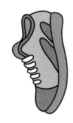

Student 3

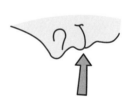

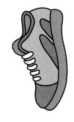

Student 4

EMC 3522
Center 4 • Mat A

Student 4

EMC 3522
Center 4 • Mat A

Student 4

EMC 3522
Center 4 • Mat A

Student 4

EMC 3522
Center 4 • Mat A

Student 4

EMC 3522
Center 4 • Mat A

Student 4

EMC 3522
Center 4 • Mat A

Student 4

EMC 3522
Center 4 • Mat A

Student 3

EMC 3522
Center 4 • Mat A

Student 3

EMC 3522
Center 4 • Mat A

Student 3

EMC 3522
Center 4 • Mat A

Student 3

EMC 3522
Center 4 • Mat A

Student 3

EMC 3522
Center 4 • Mat A

Student 3

EMC 3522
Center 4 • Mat A

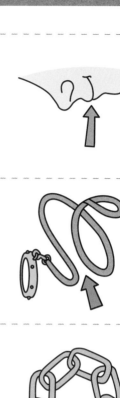

Student 6

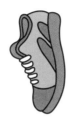
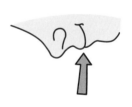

Student 5

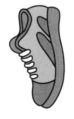

Student 6

EMC 3522
Center 4 • Mat A

Student 6

EMC 3522
Center 4 • Mat A

Student 6

EMC 3522
Center 4 • Mat A

Student 6

EMC 3522
Center 4 • Mat A

Student 6

EMC 3522
Center 4 • Mat A

Student 6

EMC 3522
Center 4 • Mat A

Student 6

EMC 3522
Center 4 • Mat A

Student 6

EMC 3522
Center 4 • Mat A

Student 5

EMC 3522
Center 4 • Mat A

Student 5

EMC 3522
Center 4 • Mat A

Student 5

EMC 3522
Center 4 • Mat A

Student 5

EMC 3522
Center 4 • Mat A

Student 5

EMC 3522
Center 4 • Mat A

Student 5

EMC 3522
Center 4 • Mat A

Student 5

EMC 3522
Center 4 • Mat A

Student 5

EMC 3522
Center 4 • Mat A

Student 6	ch	ch	sh	sh	th	th
Student 5	ch	ch	sh	sh	th	th
Student 4	ch	ch	sh	sh	th	th
Student 3	ch	ch	sh	sh	th	th
Student 2	ch	ch	sh	sh	th	th
Student 1	ch	ch	sh	sh	th	th

Student 6
EMC 3522
Center 4 • Mat B

Student 6
EMC 3522
Center 4 • Mat B

Student 6
EMC 3522
Center 4 • Mat B

Student 6
EMC 3522
Center 4 • Mat B

Student 6
EMC 3522
Center 4 • Mat B

Student 6
EMC 3522
Center 4 • Mat B

Student 5
EMC 3522
Center 4 • Mat B

Student 5
EMC 3522
Center 4 • Mat B

Student 5
EMC 3522
Center 4 • Mat B

Student 5
EMC 3522
Center 4 • Mat B

Student 5
EMC 3522
Center 4 • Mat B

Student 5
EMC 3522
Center 4 • Mat B

Student 4
EMC 3522
Center 4 • Mat B

Student 4
EMC 3522
Center 4 • Mat B

Student 4
EMC 3522
Center 4 • Mat B

Student 4
EMC 3522
Center 4 • Mat B

Student 4
EMC 3522
Center 4 • Mat B

Student 4
EMC 3522
Center 4 • Mat B

Student 3
EMC 3522
Center 4 • Mat B

Student 3
EMC 3522
Center 4 • Mat B

Student 3
EMC 3522
Center 4 • Mat B

Student 3
EMC 3522
Center 4 • Mat B

Student 3
EMC 3522
Center 4 • Mat B

Student 3
EMC 3522
Center 4 • Mat B

Student 2
EMC 3522
Center 4 • Mat B

Student 2
EMC 3522
Center 4 • Mat B

Student 2
EMC 3522
Center 4 • Mat B

Student 2
EMC 3522
Center 4 • Mat B

Student 2
EMC 3522
Center 4 • Mat B

Student 2
EMC 3522
Center 4 • Mat B

Student 1
EMC 3522
Center 4 • Mat B

Student 1
EMC 3522
Center 4 • Mat B

Student 1
EMC 3522
Center 4 • Mat B

Student 1
EMC 3522
Center 4 • Mat B

Student 1
EMC 3522
Center 4 • Mat B

Student 1
EMC 3522
Center 4 • Mat B

Practice It!

Say the word that names the picture.
Listen to the sounds of the letters in the word.
Write letters from the box on each line to spell the beginning or ending sound.

ch   sh   th

1.   b e n _____

2.   _____ e s t

3.   f i _____

4.   m o _____

5.   _____ e l l

6.   p a _____

7.    _____ e e s e

8.   _____ r e e

Read It!

Write the word or words from the box that best complete each sentence in the story.

Word Box

both	chase	crunch	push
rush	shade	teeth	thick

Chug and Thug

Beth has dogs named Chug and Thug. They are

_____ big dogs, but Chug's hair is long

and _____. Thug's hair is very short.

Chug likes to _____ after Thug. Thug

will _____ to get away. Then the dogs rest

in the _____ or under a bush. Beth gives

them bones to _____.

Beth says that Chug and Thug can do tricks. Chug

can _____ a ball with her nose. Thug can

lift his dish with his _____.

center

5

Consonant + r Blends

For the Teacher

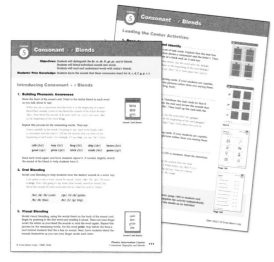

Lesson Plan

Sound Cards

Answer Keys

For the Student

front (Mat A)

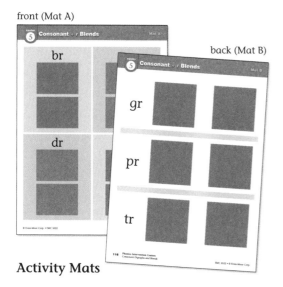

back (Mat B)

Activity Mats

Task Cards

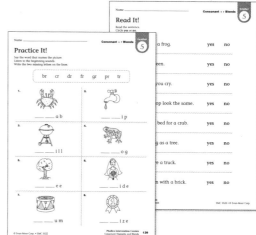

Practice and Assessment Activities

Consonant + r Blends

Objectives: Students will distinguish the *br, cr, dr, fr, gr, pr,* and *tr* blends.
Students will blend individual sounds into words.
Students will read and understand words with initial *r* blends.

Students' Prior Knowledge: Students know the sounds that these consonants stand for: *b, c, d, f, g, p, r, t.*

Introducing Consonant + *r* Blends

1. Building Phonemic Awareness

Show the front of the sound card. Point to the initial blend in each word as you talk about it. Say:

*When you see a consonant and the letter **r** at the beginning of a word, blend their sounds. Listen to me blend the sounds of the letters **b** and **r**: /br/. Now blend the sounds of **b** and **r** with me. (/br/) You hear /br/ at the beginning of the word **brag**.*

consonant + *r*

brag
drip
grin

Sound Card (front)

Repeat this process for the remaining words. Then say:

*Listen carefully to the words I'm going to say. Each word begins with a consonant and the letter **r**. Tell me the sounds that you hear at the beginning of each word. For example, if I say **tree**, you say /tr/. Listen:*

crib (/kr/)	**tray** (/tr/)	**frog** (/fr/)	**drip** (/dr/)	**brave** (/br/)
great (/gr/)	**prize** (/pr/)	**trick** (/tr/)	**crash** (/kr/)	**green** (/gr/)

Read each word again and have students repeat it. If needed, slightly stretch the sound of the blend to help students hear it.

2. Oral Blending

Model oral blending to help students hear the distinct sounds in a word. Say:

*I am going to say a word, sound by sound. Listen: /dr/ /ŏ/ /p/. The word is **drop**. Now I am going to say some other words, sound by sound. You blend the sounds for each word and tell me what the word is. Listen:*

/kr/ /ă/ /b/ (crab)	/pr/ /ī/ /d/ (pride)
/fr/ /ē/ (free)	/tr/ /ĭ/ /p/ (trip)

3. Visual Blending

Model visual blending, using the words listed on the back of the sound card. Begin by pointing to the first word and reading it aloud. Then run your finger under the letters as you blend the sounds to read the word again. Repeat this process for the remaining words. For the word **pride**, stop before the final *e* and remind students that the *e* has no sound. Next, have students blend the sounds themselves as you run your finger under each letter.

crab
free
pride
trip

Sound Card (back)

Leading the Center Activities

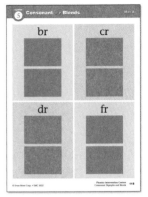

Mat A

1. Read, Discriminate, and Identify ·······························

Give each student Mat A and a set of task cards. Explain that the mat has four sections and that each section shows a consonant and the letter **r**. Then hold up the card with the picture of a brick wall on it and say:

> *This card shows a picture of some bricks. Say the word after me: **bricks**.*
> (bricks) *What sounds do you hear at the beginning of the word **bricks**?*
> (/br/) *Which letters on the mat say /**br**/?* (b-r) *Now place this card in the **b-r** section of the mat.*

Repeat this process with the remaining cards. If your students are capable, have them tell you the names of the pictures rather than you saying them. (brown, crib, crown, dress, drum, frog, fruit)

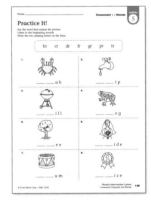

Mat B

2. Read and Understand ··

Have students turn over their mats. Distribute the task cards for Mat B. Point out the three rows of blends on the mat and review the sounds that each blend stands for: **/gr/**, **/pr/**, **/tr/**. Then hold up the card with the picture of grapes on it and say:

> *This card shows a picture of grapes. Say the word after me: **grapes**.*
> (grapes) *What sounds do you hear at the beginning of the word **grapes**?*
> (/gr/) *Which letters on the mat say /**gr**/?* (g-r) *Now place this card in the row for **g-r**.*

Repeat this process with the remaining cards. If your students are capable, have them tell you the names of the pictures rather than you saying them. (green, present, pretzel, train, truck)

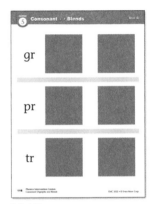

Page 139

3. Practice the Skill ···

Distribute the Practice It! activity (page 139) to students. Read the directions aloud. Then say:

> *Look at the first picture. It is a crab. Say the sounds that you hear at the beginning of the word **crab**.* (/kr/) *What letters say /**kr**/?* (c-r)
> *Write the letters **c-r** on the lines under the picture. Now let's blend the sounds and read the word: /kr/ /ă/ /b/ crab.*

Repeat this process to complete the page.

Page 140

Apply and Assess

After the lesson, distribute the Read It! activity (page 140) to students and read the directions aloud. Have students complete the activity independently. Then listen to them read the sentences. Use the results as an informal assessment of students' skill mastery.

consonant + r

brag
drip
grin

EMC 3522

Center 5 • Sound Card

Answer Keys

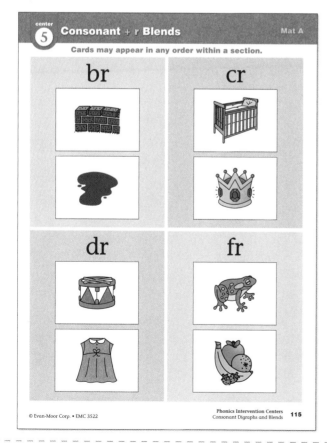

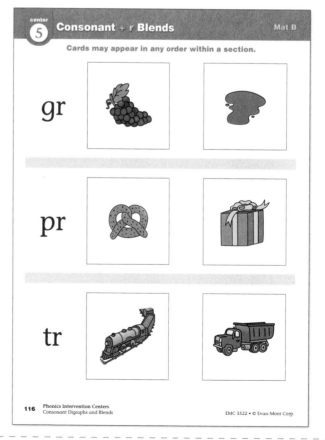

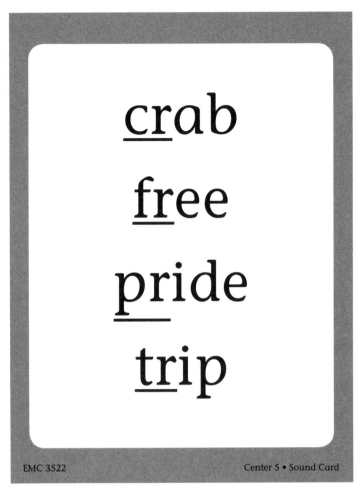

crab

free

pride

trip

EMC 3522   Center 5 • Sound Card

Answer Keys

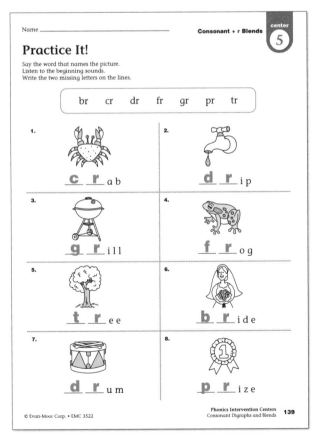

Name _____   **Consonant + r Blends**   center 5

Practice It!

Say the word that names the picture.
Listen to the beginning sounds.
Write the two missing letters on the lines.

br   cr   dr   fr   gr   pr   tr

1. **c r** a b

2. **d r** i p

3. **g r** i l l

4. **f r** o g

5. **t r** e e

6. **b r** i d e

7. **d r** u m

8. **p r** i z e

© Evan-Moor Corp. • EMC 3522   Phonics Intervention Centers
                                                Consonant Digraphs and Blends   **139**

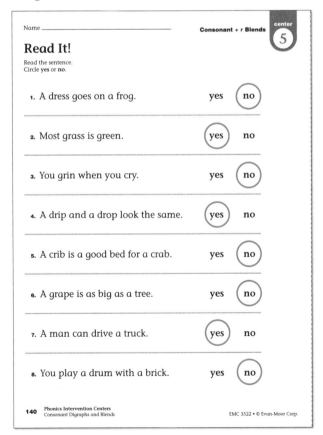

Name _____   **Consonant + r Blends**   center 5

Read It!

Read the sentence.
Circle **yes** or **no**.

1. A dress goes on a frog.   yes   (no)

2. Most grass is green.   (yes)   no

3. You grin when you cry.   yes   (no)

4. A drip and a drop look the same.   (yes)   no

5. A crib is a good bed for a crab.   yes   (no)

6. A grape is as big as a tree.   yes   (no)

7. A man can drive a truck.   (yes)   no

8. You play a drum with a brick.   yes   (no)

140   Phonics Intervention Centers
           Consonant Digraphs and Blends   EMC 3522 • © Evan-Moor Corp.

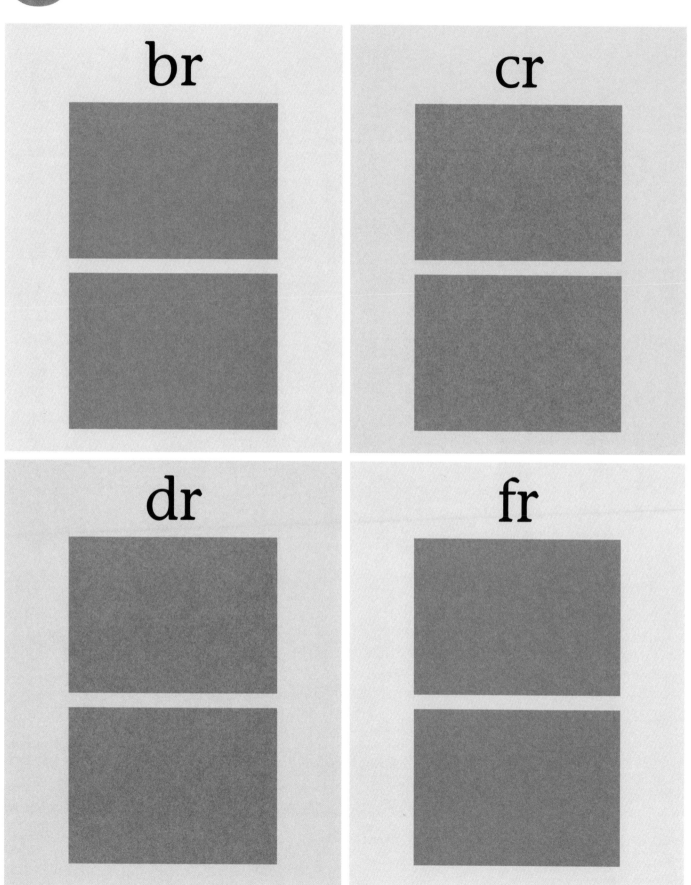

gr

pr

tr

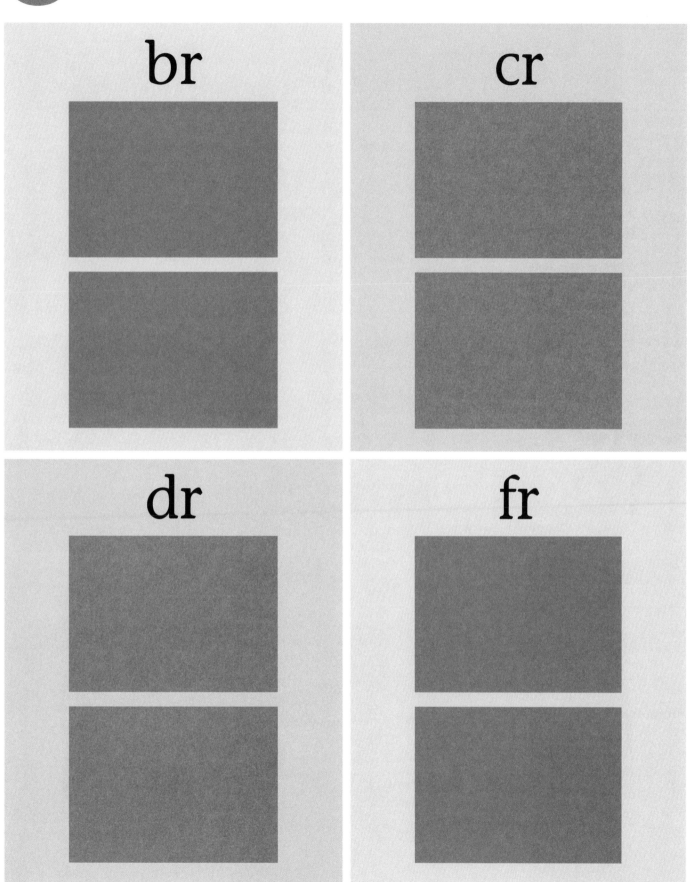

br

cr

dr

fr

gr

pr

tr

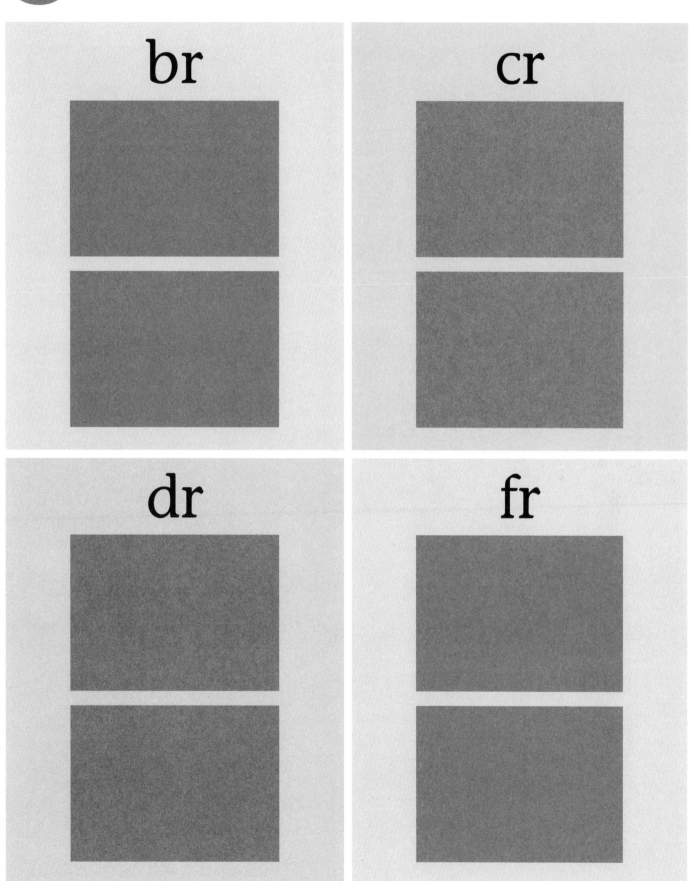

br

cr

dr

fr

gr

pr

tr

Phonics Intervention Centers
Consonant Digraphs and Blends

EMC 3522 • © Evan-Moor Corp.

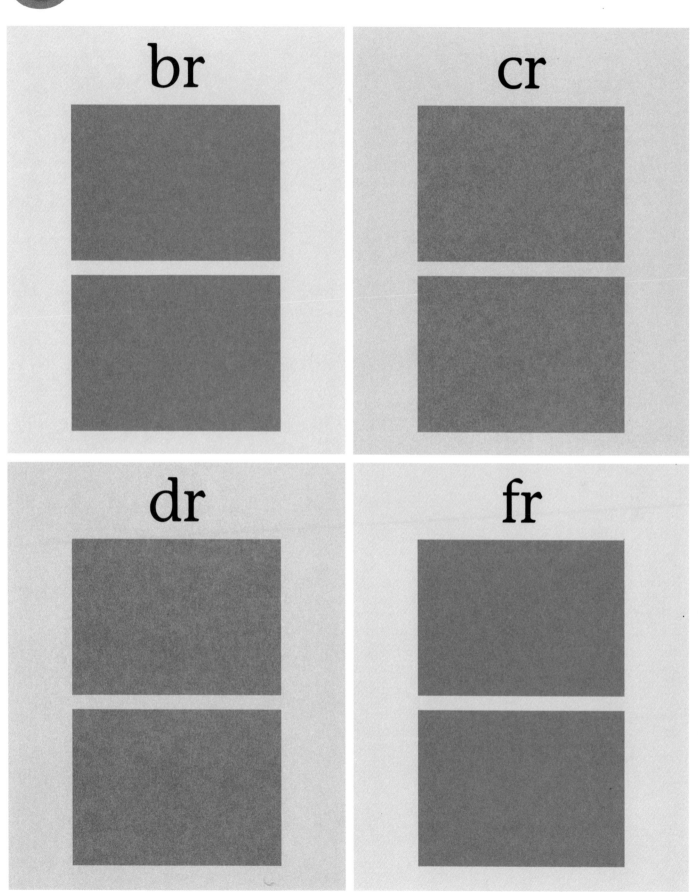

br

cr

dr

fr

gr

pr

tr

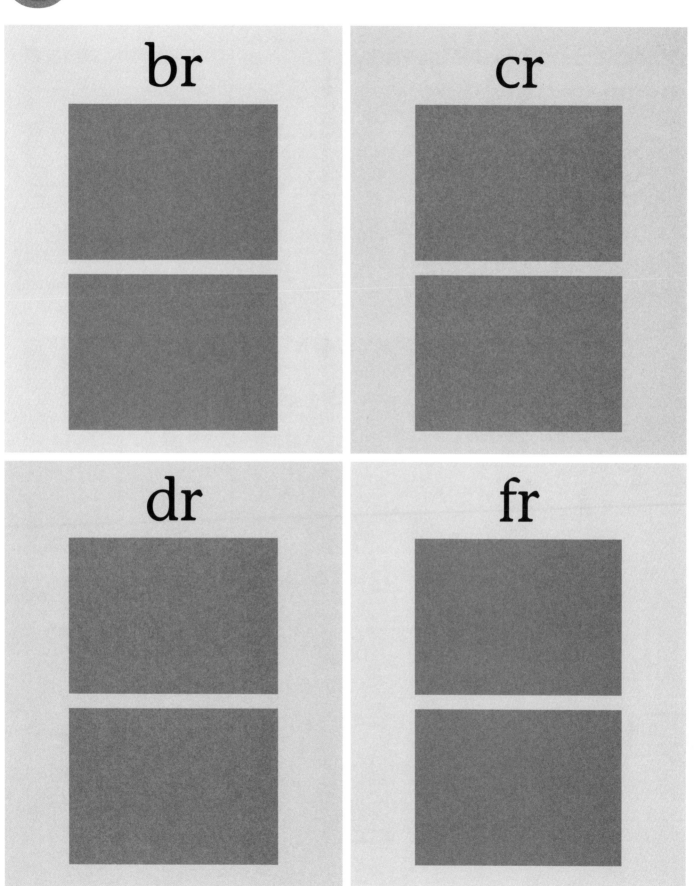

br

cr

dr

fr

gr

pr

tr

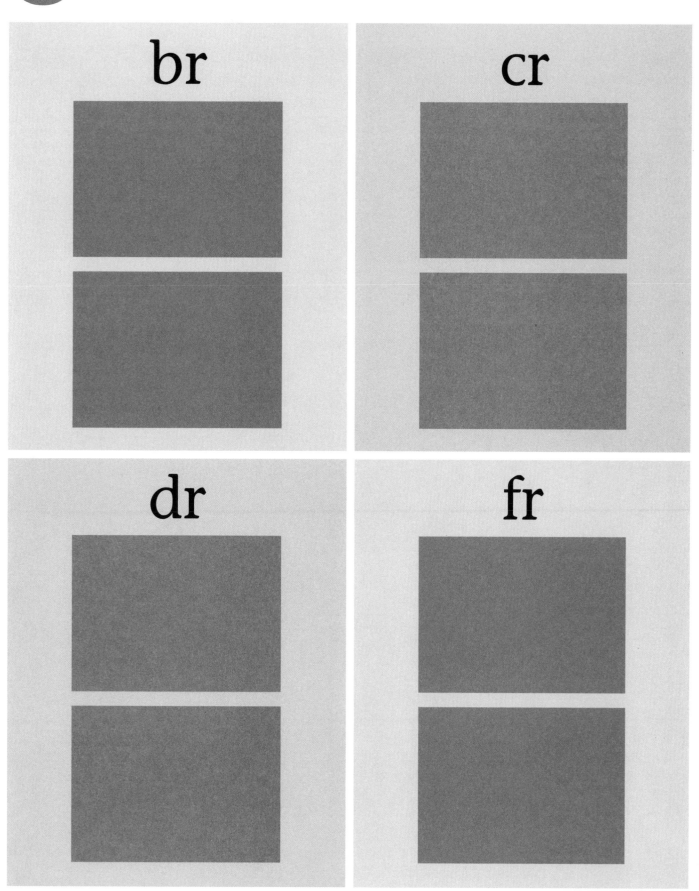

br

cr

dr

fr

Phonics Intervention Centers
Consonant Digraphs and Blends **125**

gr

pr

tr

Phonics Intervention Centers
Consonant Digraphs and Blends

Student 2

Student 1

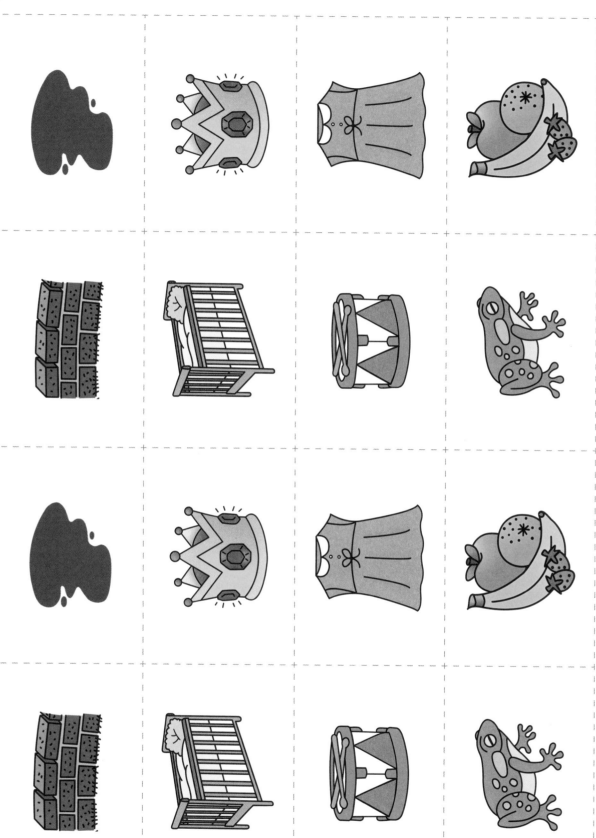

Student 2

EMC 3522 • Center 5 • Mat A

Student 2

EMC 3522 • Center 5 • Mat A

Student 2

EMC 3522 • Center 5 • Mat A

Student 2

EMC 3522 • Center 5 • Mat A

Student 2

EMC 3522 • Center 5 • Mat A

Student 2

EMC 3522 • Center 5 • Mat A

Student 2

EMC 3522 • Center 5 • Mat A

Student 1

EMC 3522 • Center 5 • Mat A

Student 1

EMC 3522 • Center 5 • Mat A

Student 1

EMC 3522 • Center 5 • Mat A

Student 1

EMC 3522 • Center 5 • Mat A

Student 1

EMC 3522 • Center 5 • Mat A

Student 1

EMC 3522 • Center 5 • Mat A

Student 1

EMC 3522 • Center 5 • Mat A

Student 4

  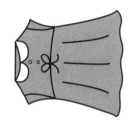 

  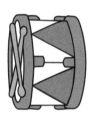 

Student 3

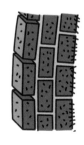  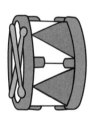 

Student 4

EMC 3522 • Center 5 • Mat A

Student 4

EMC 3522 • Center 5 • Mat A

Student 4

EMC 3522 • Center 5 • Mat A

Student 4

EMC 3522 • Center 5 • Mat A

Student 4

EMC 3522 • Center 5 • Mat A

Student 4

EMC 3522 • Center 5 • Mat A

Student 3

EMC 3522 • Center 5 • Mat A

Student 3

EMC 3522 • Center 5 • Mat A

Student 3

EMC 3522 • Center 5 • Mat A

Student 3

EMC 3522 • Center 5 • Mat A

Student 3

EMC 3522 • Center 5 • Mat A

Student 3

EMC 3522 • Center 5 • Mat A

Student 6

Student 5

Phonics Intervention Centers
Consonant Digraphs and Blends **131**

Student 6

EMC 3522 • Center 5 • Mat A

Student 6

EMC 3522 • Center 5 • Mat A

Student 6

EMC 3522 • Center 5 • Mat A

Student 6

EMC 3522 • Center 5 • Mat A

Student 6

EMC 3522 • Center 5 • Mat A

Student 6

EMC 3522 • Center 5 • Mat A

Student 6

EMC 3522 • Center 5 • Mat A

Student 6

EMC 3522 • Center 5 • Mat A

Student 5

EMC 3522 • Center 5 • Mat A

Student 5

EMC 3522 • Center 5 • Mat A

Student 5

EMC 3522 • Center 5 • Mat A

Student 5

EMC 3522 • Center 5 • Mat A

Student 5

EMC 3522 • Center 5 • Mat A

Student 5

EMC 3522 • Center 5 • Mat A

Student 5

EMC 3522 • Center 5 • Mat A

Student 5

EMC 3522 • Center 5 • Mat A

EMC 3522 • © Evan-Moor Corp.

Student 2

Student 1

Student 2

EMC 3522 • Center 5 • Mat B

Student 2

EMC 3522 • Center 5 • Mat B

Student 2

EMC 3522 • Center 5 • Mat B

Student 2

EMC 3522 • Center 5 • Mat B

Student 2

EMC 3522 • Center 5 • Mat B

Student 2

EMC 3522 • Center 5 • Mat B

Student 1

EMC 3522 • Center 5 • Mat B

Student 1

EMC 3522 • Center 5 • Mat B

Student 1

EMC 3522 • Center 5 • Mat B

Student 1

EMC 3522 • Center 5 • Mat B

Student 1

EMC 3522 • Center 5 • Mat B

Student 1

EMC 3522 • Center 5 • Mat B

Student 4

Student 3

Student 4

EMC 3522 • Center 5 • Mat B

Student 4

EMC 3522 • Center 5 • Mat B

Student 4

EMC 3522 • Center 5 • Mat B

Student 4

EMC 3522 • Center 5 • Mat B

Student 4

EMC 3522 • Center 5 • Mat B

Student 3

EMC 3522 • Center 5 • Mat B

Student 4

EMC 3522 • Center 5 • Mat B

Student 3

EMC 3522 • Center 5 • Mat B

Student 3

EMC 3522 • Center 5 • Mat B

Student 3

EMC 3522 • Center 5 • Mat B

Student 3

EMC 3522 • Center 5 • Mat B

Student 3

EMC 3522 • Center 5 • Mat B

Student 6

Student 5

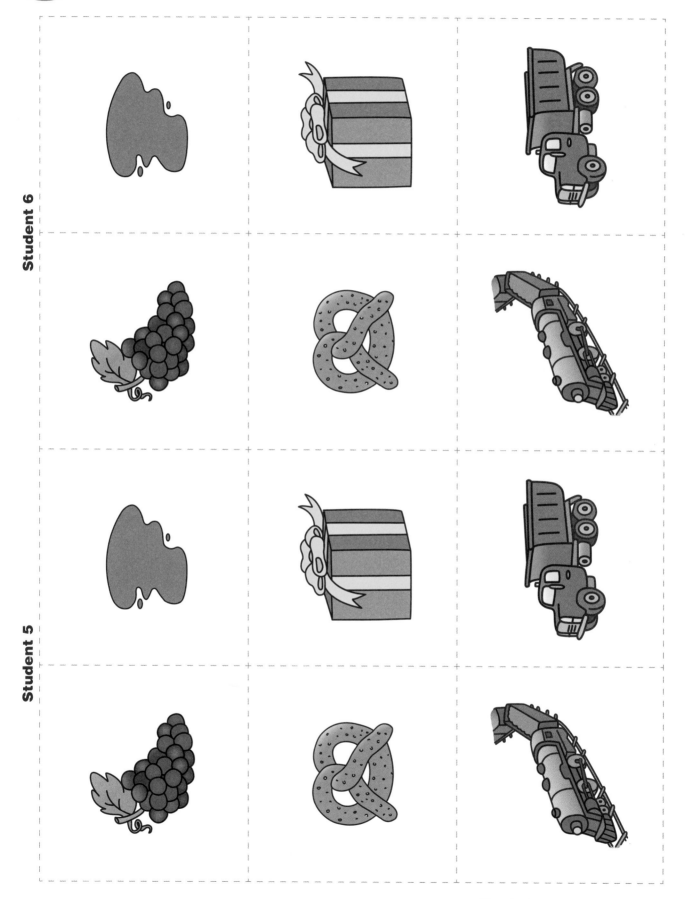

Phonics Intervention Centers
Consonant Digraphs and Blends

137

Task Cards

Student 6

EMC 3522 • Center 5 • Mat B

Student 6

EMC 3522 • Center 5 • Mat B

Student 6

EMC 3522 • Center 5 • Mat B

Student 6

EMC 3522 • Center 5 • Mat B

Student 6

EMC 3522 • Center 5 • Mat B

Student 6

EMC 3522 • Center 5 • Mat B

Student 5

EMC 3522 • Center 5 • Mat B

Student 5

EMC 3522 • Center 5 • Mat B

Student 5

EMC 3522 • Center 5 • Mat B

Student 5

EMC 3522 • Center 5 • Mat B

Student 5

EMC 3522 • Center 5 • Mat B

Student 5

EMC 3522 • Center 5 • Mat B

Practice It!

Say the word that names the picture.
Listen to the beginning sounds.
Write the two missing letters on the lines.

| br | cr | dr | fr | gr | pr | tr |

1.

_____ _____ a b

2.

_____ _____ i p

3.

_____ _____ i l l

4.

_____ _____ o g

5.

_____ _____ e e

6.

_____ _____ i d e

7.

_____ _____ u m

8.

_____ _____ i z e

Read It!

Read the sentence.
Circle **yes** or **no**.

1. A dress goes on a frog.   yes   no

2. Most grass is green.   yes   no

3. You grin when you cry.   yes   no

4. A drip and a drop look the same.   yes   no

5. A crib is a good bed for a crab.   yes   no

6. A grape is as big as a tree.   yes   no

7. A man can drive a truck.   yes   no

8. You play a drum with a brick.   yes   no

Consonant + l Blends

For the Teacher

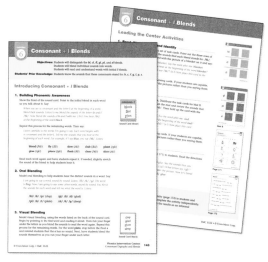

Lesson Plan

Sound Cards

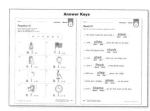

Answer Keys

For the Student

front (Mat A)

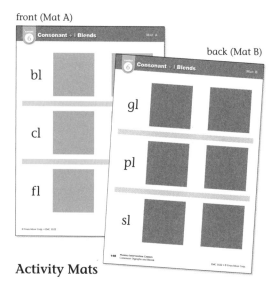

back (Mat B)

Activity Mats

Task Cards

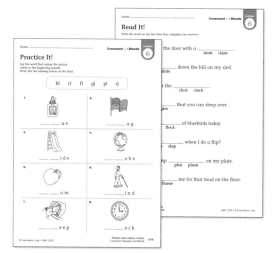

Practice and Assessment Activities

EMC 3522 • © Evan-Moor Corp.

center 6 — Consonant + l Blends

Objectives: Students will distinguish the *bl*, *cl*, *fl*, *gl*, *pl*, and *sl* blends.
Students will blend individual sounds into words.
Students will read and understand words with initial *l* blends.

Students' Prior Knowledge: Students know the sounds that these consonants stand for: *b, c, f, g, l, p, s.*

Introducing Consonant + *l* Blends

1. Building Phonemic Awareness

Show the front of the sound card. Point to the initial blend in each word as you talk about it. Say:

*When you see a consonant and the letter **l** at the beginning of a word, blend their sounds. Listen to me blend the sounds of the letters **b** and **l**: /bl/. Now blend the sounds of **b** and **l** with me. (/bl/) You hear /bl/ at the beginning of the word **block**.*

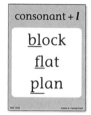

Sound Card (front)

Repeat this process for the remaining words. Then say:

*Listen carefully to the words I'm going to say. Each word begins with a consonant and the letter **l**. Tell me the sounds that you hear at the beginning of each word. For example, if I say **blue**, you say /bl/. Listen:*

blood (/bl/)	**fly** (/fl/)	**slow** (/sl/)	**club** (/kl/)	**plant** (/pl/)
glue (/gl/)	**place** (/pl/)	**flash** (/fl/)	**class** (/kl/)	**slice** (/sl/)

Read each word again and have students repeat it. If needed, slightly stretch the sound of the blend to help students hear it.

2. Oral Blending

Model oral blending to help students hear the distinct sounds in a word. Say:

*I am going to say a word, sound by sound. Listen: /fl/ /ă/ /g/. The word is **flag**. Now I am going to say some other words, sound by sound. You blend the sounds for each word and tell me what the word is. Listen:*

/kl/ /ă/ /p/ (clap)	/gl/ /ă/ /d/ (glad)
/pl/ /ā/ /t/ (plate)	/sl/ /ē/ /p/ (sleep)

3. Visual Blending

Model visual blending, using the words listed on the back of the sound card. Begin by pointing to the first word and reading it aloud. Then run your finger under the letters as you blend the sounds to read the word again. Repeat this process for the remaining words. For the word **plate**, stop before the final *e* and remind students that the *e* has no sound. Next, have students blend the sounds themselves as you run your finger under each letter.

Sound Card (back)

© Evan-Moor Corp. • EMC 3522

Phonics Intervention Centers
Consonant Digraphs and Blends **143**

Consonant + l Blends *(continued)*

Leading the Center Activities

1. Read, Discriminate, and Identify ....

Give each student Mat A and a set of task cards. Point out the three rows of blends on the mat and review the sounds that each blend stands for: **/bl/**, **/kl/**, **/fl/**. Then hold up the card with the picture of a blanket on it and say:

*This card shows a picture of a blanket. Say the word after me: **blanket**. (blanket) What sounds do you hear at the beginning of the word **blanket**? (/bl/) Which letters on the mat say /**bl**/? (b-l) Now place this card in the row for **b-l**.*

Repeat this process with the remaining cards. If your students are capable, have them tell you the names of the pictures rather than you saying them. (black, cloud, clown, flag, floor)

2. Read and Understand ....

Have students turn over their mats. Distribute the task cards for Mat B. Point out the three rows of blends on the mat and review the sounds that each blend stands for: **/gl/**, **/pl/**, **/sl/**. Then hold up the card with the picture of a sled on it and say:

*This card shows a picture of a sled. Say the word after me: **sled**. (sled) What sounds do you hear at the beginning of the word **sled**? (/sl/) Which letters on the mat say /**sl**/? (s-l) Now place this card in the row for **s-l**.*

Repeat this process with the remaining cards. If your students are capable, have them tell you the names of the pictures rather than you saying them. (glass, glove, plane, plug, slide)

3. Practice the Skill ....

Distribute the Practice It! activity (page 171) to students. Read the directions aloud. Then say:

*Look at the first picture. It is a bottle of glue. Say the sounds that you hear at the beginning of the word **glue**. (/gl/) What letters say /**gl**/? (g-l) Write the letters **g-l** on the lines under the picture. Now let's blend the sounds and read the word: /gl/ /o͞o/ **glue**.*

Repeat this process to complete the page.

Apply and Assess

After the lesson, distribute the Read It! activity (page 172) to students and read the directions aloud. Have students complete the activity independently. Then listen to them read the sentences. Use the results as an informal assessment of students' skill mastery.

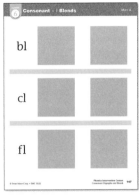

Mat A

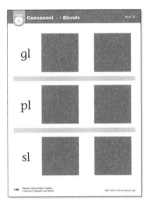

Mat B

Page 171

Page 172

consonant + **l**

<u>b</u>lock

<u>fl</u>at

<u>p</u>lan

EMC 3522

Center 6 • Sound Card

Answer Keys

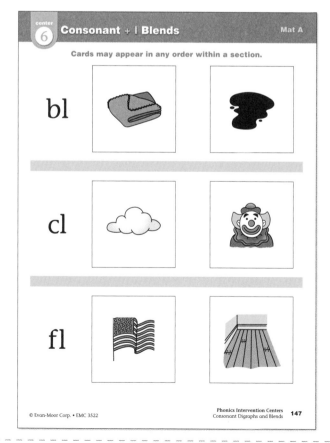

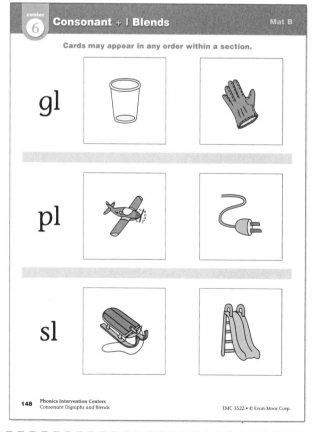

clap

glad

plate

sleep

EMC 3522

Center 6 • Sound Card

Answer Keys

Name _____

Consonant + l Blends

center 6

Practice It!

Say the word that names the picture.
Listen to the beginning sounds.
Write the two missing letters on the lines.

bl	cl	fl	gl	pl	sl

1. **g l** u e

2. **f l** a g

3. **s l** i d e

4. **g l** o b e

5. **p l** u m

6. **b l** i n d

7. **s l** e e p

8. **c l** o c k

© Evan-Moor Corp. • EMC 3522

Phonics Intervention Centers
Consonant Digraphs and Blends **171**

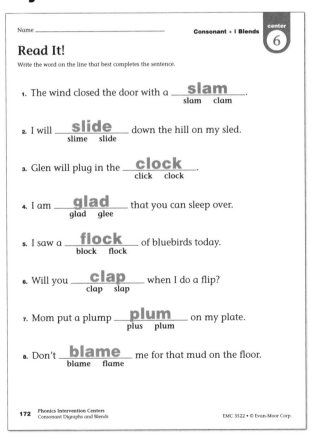

Name _____

Consonant + l Blends

center 6

Read It!

Write the word on the line that best completes the sentence.

1. The wind closed the door with a ___**slam**___.
   slam   clam

2. I will ___**slide**___ down the hill on my sled.
   slime   slide

3. Glen will plug in the ___**clock**___.
   click   clock

4. I am ___**glad**___ that you can sleep over.
   glad   glee

5. I saw a ___**flock**___ of bluebirds today.
   block   flock

6. Will you ___**clap**___ when I do a flip?
   clap   slap

7. Mom put a plump ___**plum**___ on my plate.
   plus   plum

8. Don't ___**blame**___ me for that mud on the floor.
   blame   flame

172 Phonics Intervention Centers
Consonant Digraphs and Blends

EMC 3522 • © Evan-Moor Corp.

bl

cl

fl

gl

pl

sl

bl

cl

fl

gl

pl

sl

bl

cl

fl

gl

pl

sl

Consonant + l Blends

Mat A

bl

cl

fl

© Evan-Moor Corp. • EMC 3522

Phonics Intervention Centers
Consonant Digraphs and Blends **153**

gl

pl

sl

bl

cl

fl

gl

pl

sl

bl

cl

fl

gl

pl

sl

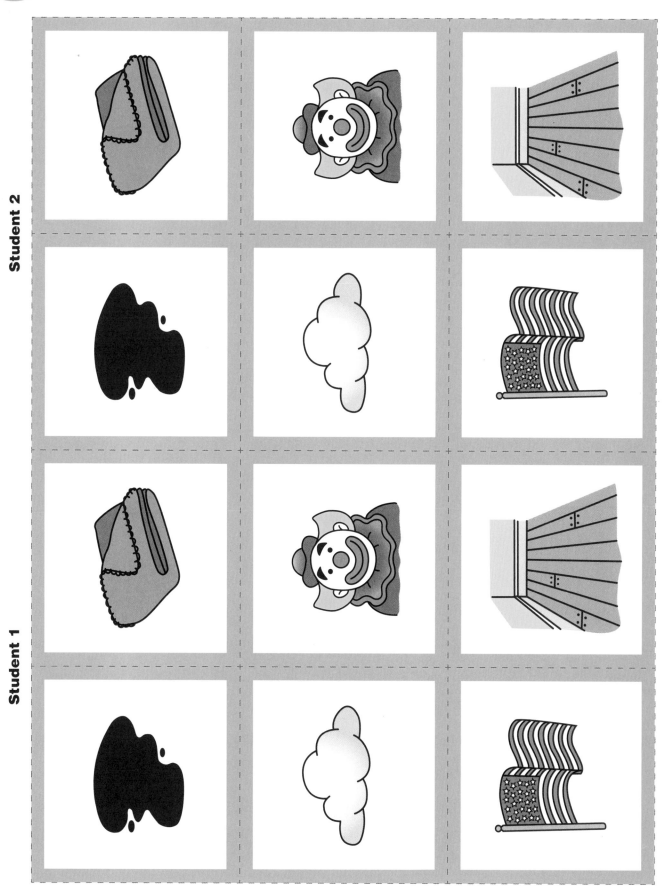

Student 2

Student 1

Student 2

EMC 3522 • Center 6 • Mat A

Student 2

EMC 3522 • Center 6 • Mat A

Student 2

EMC 3522 • Center 6 • Mat A

Student 2

EMC 3522 • Center 6 • Mat A

Student 2

EMC 3522 • Center 6 • Mat A

Student 1

EMC 3522 • Center 6 • Mat A

Student 2

EMC 3522 • Center 6 • Mat A

Student 1

EMC 3522 • Center 6 • Mat A

Student 1

EMC 3522 • Center 6 • Mat A

Student 1

EMC 3522 • Center 6 • Mat A

Student 1

EMC 3522 • Center 6 • Mat A

Student 1

EMC 3522 • Center 6 • Mat A

Phonics Intervention Centers
Consonant Digraphs and Blends

EMC 3522 • © Evan-Moor Corp.

center
6

Student 4

Student 3

Phonics Intervention Centers
Consonant Digraphs and Blends

161

EMC 3522 • Center 6 • Mat A

Student 4

EMC 3522 • Center 6 • Mat A

Student 4

EMC 3522 • Center 6 • Mat A

Student 4

EMC 3522 • Center 6 • Mat A

Student 4

EMC 3522 • Center 6 • Mat A

Student 4

EMC 3522 • Center 6 • Mat A

Student 3

EMC 3522 • Center 6 • Mat A

Student 3

EMC 3522 • Center 6 • Mat A

Student 3

EMC 3522 • Center 6 • Mat A

Student 3

EMC 3522 • Center 6 • Mat A

Student 3

EMC 3522 • Center 6 • Mat A

Student 3

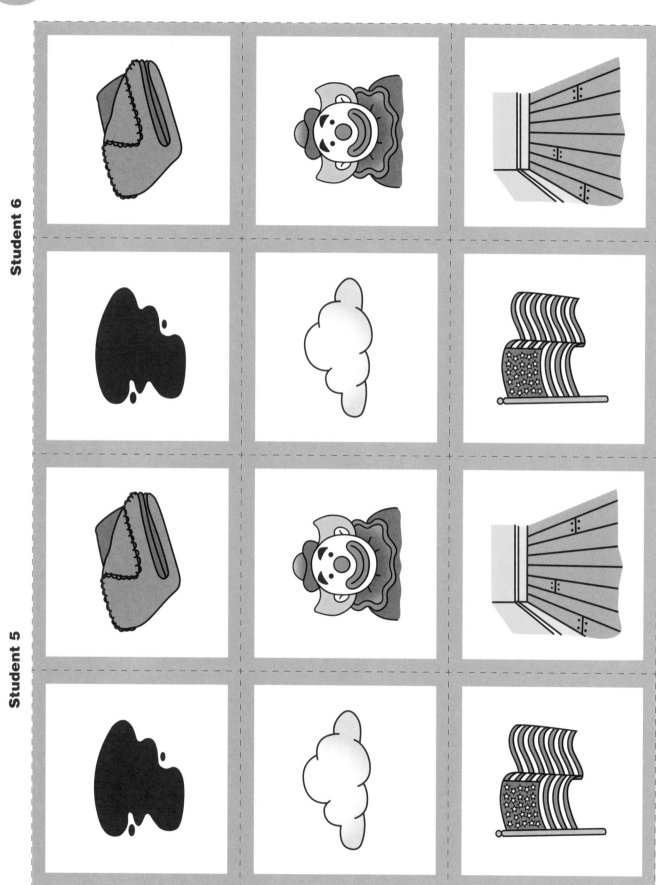

Student 6

Student 5

Student 6

Student 6

Student 6

Student 6

Student 6

Student 5

Student 5

Student 5

Student 5

Student 5

Student 2

Student 1

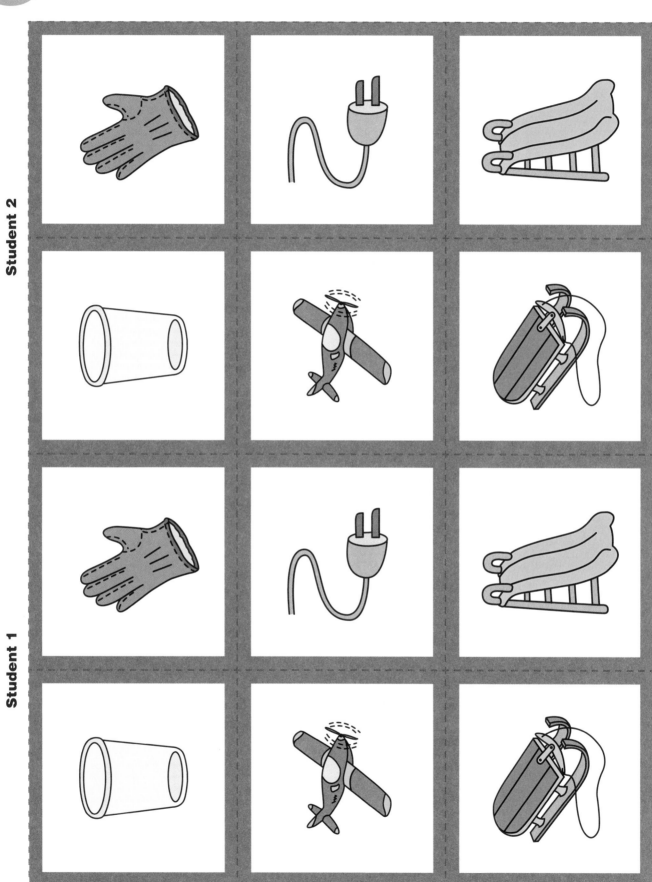

Student 2

EMC 3522 • Center 6 • Mat B

Student 2

EMC 3522 • Center 6 • Mat B

Student 2

EMC 3522 • Center 6 • Mat B

Student 2

EMC 3522 • Center 6 • Mat B

Student 2

EMC 3522 • Center 6 • Mat B

Student 2

EMC 3522 • Center 6 • Mat B

Student 1

EMC 3522 • Center 6 • Mat B

Student 1

EMC 3522 • Center 6 • Mat B

Student 1

EMC 3522 • Center 6 • Mat B

Student 1

EMC 3522 • Center 6 • Mat B

Student 1

EMC 3522 • Center 6 • Mat B

Student 1

EMC 3522 • Center 6 • Mat B

Phonics Intervention Centers
Consonant Digraphs and Blends

EMC 3522 • © Evan-Moor Corp.

Student 4

Student 3

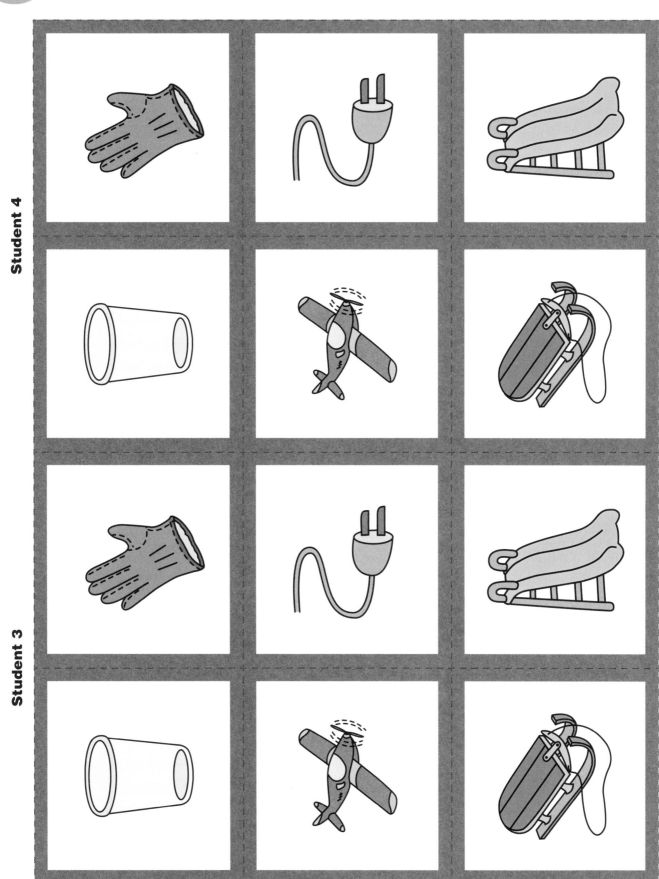

Student 4

EMC 3522 • Center 6 • Mat B

Student 4

EMC 3522 • Center 6 • Mat B

Student 4

EMC 3522 • Center 6 • Mat B

Student 4

EMC 3522 • Center 6 • Mat B

Student 4

EMC 3522 • Center 6 • Mat B

Student 4

EMC 3522 • Center 6 • Mat B

Student 3

EMC 3522 • Center 6 • Mat B

Student 3

EMC 3522 • Center 6 • Mat B

Student 3

EMC 3522 • Center 6 • Mat B

Student 3

EMC 3522 • Center 6 • Mat B

Student 3

EMC 3522 • Center 6 • Mat B

Student 3

EMC 3522 • Center 6 • Mat B

Student 6

Student 5

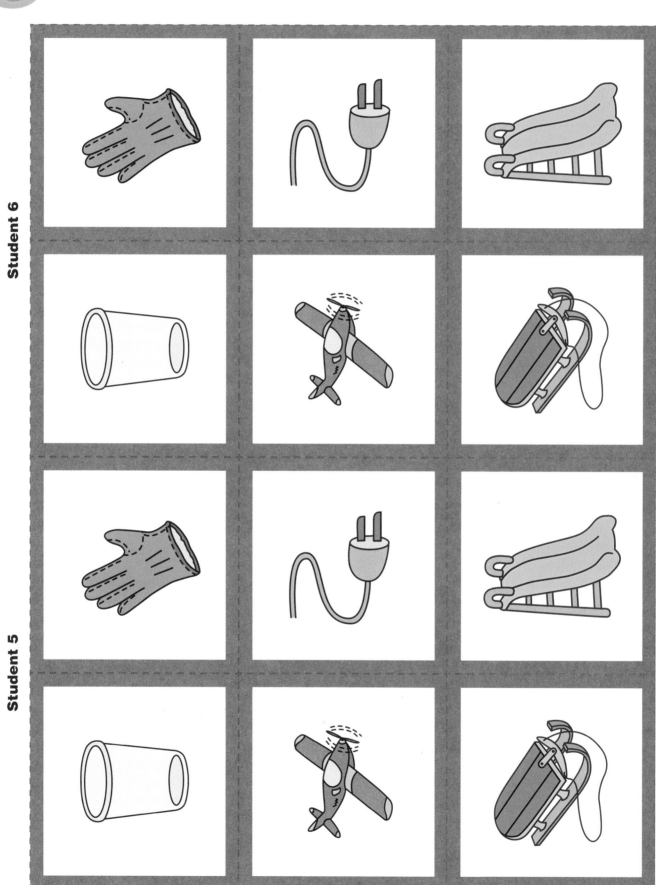

Student 6

EMC 3522 • Center 6 • Mat B

Student 6

EMC 3522 • Center 6 • Mat B

Student 6

EMC 3522 • Center 6 • Mat B

Student 6

EMC 3522 • Center 6 • Mat B

Student 6

EMC 3522 • Center 6 • Mat B

Student 6

EMC 3522 • Center 6 • Mat B

Student 5

EMC 3522 • Center 6 • Mat B

Student 5

EMC 3522 • Center 6 • Mat B

Student 5

EMC 3522 • Center 6 • Mat B

Student 5

EMC 3522 • Center 6 • Mat B

Student 5

EMC 3522 • Center 6 • Mat B

Student 5

EMC 3522 • Center 6 • Mat B

Practice It!

Say the word that names the picture.
Listen to the beginning sounds.
Write the two missing letters on the lines.

| bl | cl | fl | gl | pl | sl |

1.

_____ _____ u e

2.

_____ _____ a g

3.

_____ _____ i d e

4.

_____ _____ o b e

5.

_____ _____ u m

6.

_____ _____ i n d

7.

_____ _____ e e p

8.

_____ _____ o c k

Read It!

Write the word on the line that best completes the sentence.

1. The wind closed the door with a _____.
   slam   clam

2. I will _____ down the hill on my sled.
   slime   slide

3. Glen will plug in the _____.
   click   clock

4. I am _____ that you can sleep over.
   glad   glee

5. I saw a _____ of bluebirds today.
   block   flock

6. Will you _____ when I do a flip?
   clap   slap

7. Mom put a plump _____ on my plate.
   plus   plum

8. Don't _____ me for that mud on the floor.
   blame   flame

center 7

Initial s Blends

For the Teacher

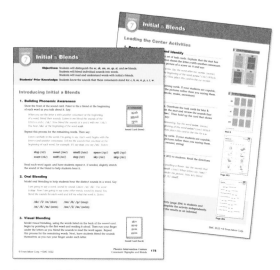

Lesson Plan

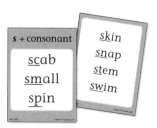

Sound Cards

s + consonant

scab
small
spin

skin
snap
stem
swim

Answer Keys

For the Student

front (Mat A)

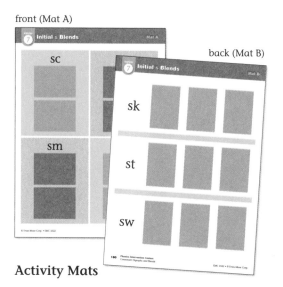

back (Mat B)

Activity Mats

Task Cards

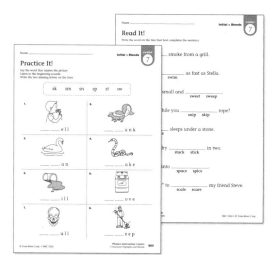

Practice and Assessment Activities

Initial s Blends

Objectives: Students will distinguish the *sc*, *sk*, *sm*, *sn*, *sp*, *st*, and *sw* blends.
Students will blend individual sounds into words.
Students will read and understand words with initial *s* blends.

Students' Prior Knowledge: Students know the sounds that these consonants stand for: *c, k, m, n, p, s, t, w.*

Introducing Initial *s* Blends

1. Building Phonemic Awareness

Show the front of the sound card. Point to the *s* blend at the beginning of each word as you talk about it. Say:

*When you see the letter **s** with another consonant at the beginning of a word, blend their sounds. Listen to me blend the sounds of the letters **s** and **c**: /sk/. Now blend the sounds of **s** and **c** with me. (/sk/) You hear /sk/ at the beginning of the word **scab**.*

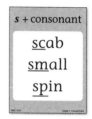

Sound Card (front)

Repeat this process for the remaining words. Then say:

*Listen carefully to the words I'm going to say. Each word begins with the letter **s** and another consonant. Tell me the sounds that you hear at the beginning of each word. For example, if I say **star**, you say /st/. Listen:*

stop (/st/)	**sweet** (/sw/)	**smell** (/sm/)	**space** (/sp/)	**spill** (/sp/)
scare (/sk/)	**sniff** (/sn/)	**step** (/st/)	**sky** (/sk/)	**skip** (/sk/)

Read each word again and have students repeat it. If needed, slightly stretch the sound of the blend to help students hear it.

2. Oral Blending

Model oral blending to help students hear the distinct sounds in a word. Say:

*I am going to say a word, sound by sound. Listen: /st/ /ā/. The word is **stay**. Now I am going to say some other words, sound by sound. You blend the sounds for each word and tell me what the word is. Listen:*

/sk/ /ĭ/ /n/ (skin)	/sn/ /ă/ /p/ (snap)
/st/ /ĕ/ /m/ (stem)	/sw/ /ĭ/ /m/ (swim)

3. Visual Blending

Model visual blending, using the words listed on the back of the sound card. Begin by pointing to the first word and reading it aloud. Then run your finger under the letters as you blend the sounds to read the word again. Repeat this process for the remaining words. Next, have students blend the sounds themselves as you run your finger under each letter.

Sound Card (back)

Leading the Center Activities

1. Read, Discriminate, and Identify ....

Give each student Mat A and a set of task cards. Explain that the mat has four sections and that each section shows the letter **s** with another consonant. Then hold up the card with the picture of a screw on it and say:

*This card shows a picture of a screw. Say the word after me: **screw**. (screw) What sounds do you hear at the beginning of the word **screw**? (/sk/) Which letters on the mat say /sk/? (s-c) Now place this card in the **s-c** section of the mat.*

Repeat this process with the remaining cards. If your students are capable, have them tell you the names of the pictures rather than you saying them. (scarecrow, spider, spoon, smile, smoke, snake, snowman)

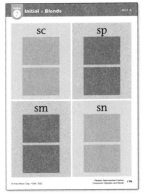

Mat A

2. Read and Understand ....

Have students turn over their mats. Distribute the task cards for Mat B. Point out the three rows of blends on the mat and review the sounds that each blend stands for: **/sk/, /st/, /sw/**. Then hold up the card that shows the picture of a girl swimming and say:

*This card shows a picture of a girl swimming. Say the word **swim**. (swim) What sounds do you hear at the beginning of the word **swim**? (/sw/) Which letters on the mat say /sw/? (s-w) Now place this card in the row for **s-w**.*

Repeat this process with the remaining cards. If your students are capable, have them tell you the names of the pictures rather than you saying them. (skate, skirt, skunk, stamp, star, store, sweater, swing)

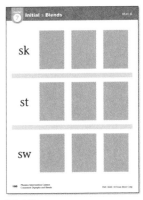

Mat B

3. Practice the Skill ....

Distribute the Practice It! activity (page 203) to students. Read the directions aloud. Then say:

*Look at the first picture. It shows a boy smelling a flower. Say the sounds that you hear at the beginning of the word **smell**. (/sm/) What letters say /sm/? (s-m) Write the letters **s-m** on the lines under the picture. Now let's blend the sounds and read the word: /sm/ /ĕ/ /l/ **smell**.*

Repeat this process to complete the page.

Page 203

Apply and Assess

After the lesson, distribute the Read It! activity (page 204) to students and read the directions aloud. Have students complete the activity independently. Then listen to them read the sentences. Use the results as an informal assessment of students' skill mastery.

Page 204

s + consonant

scab
small
spin

EMC 3522

Center 7 • Sound Card

Answer Keys

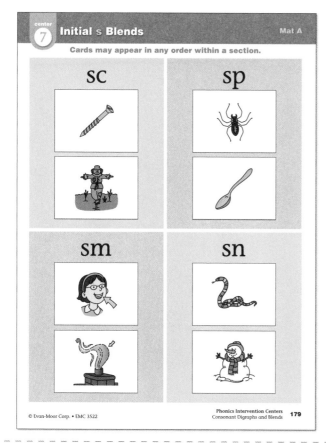

EMC 3522

skin

snap

stem

swim

Answer Keys

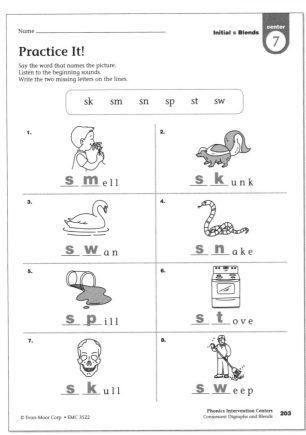

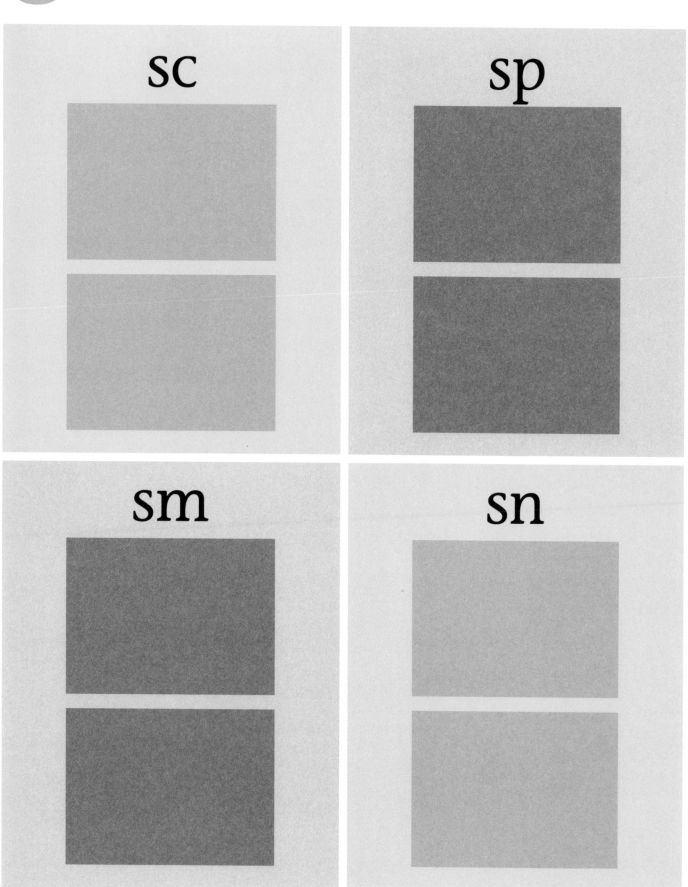

sc

sp

sm

sn

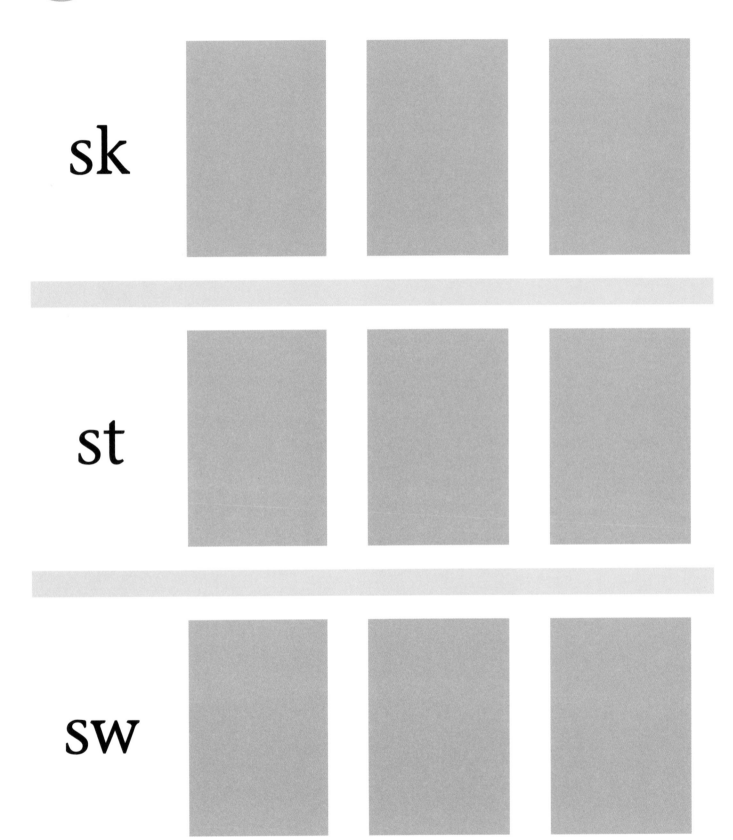

sk

st

sw

Phonics Intervention Centers
Consonant Digraphs and Blends

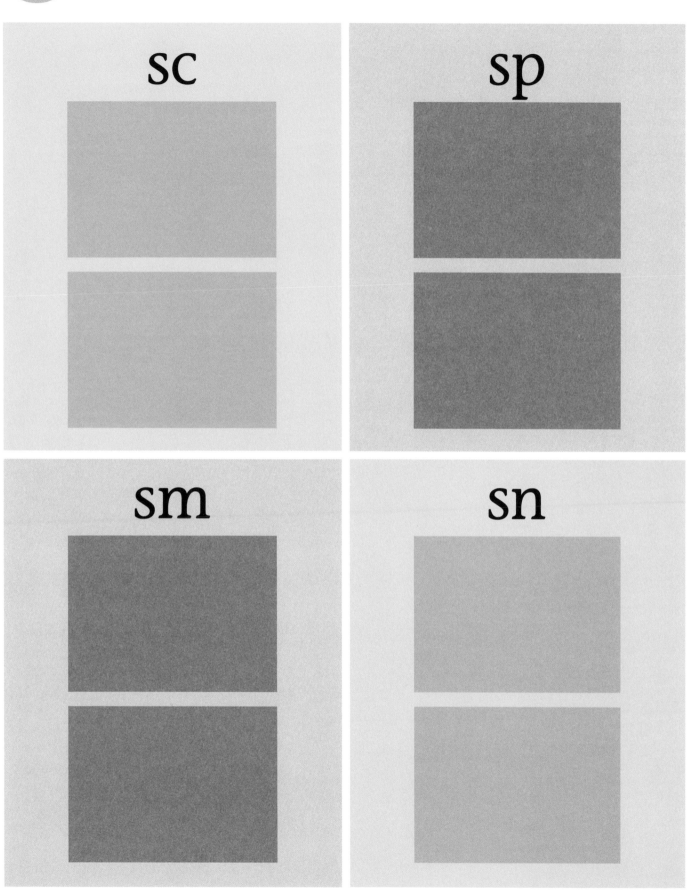

sc

sp

sm

sn

sk

st

sw

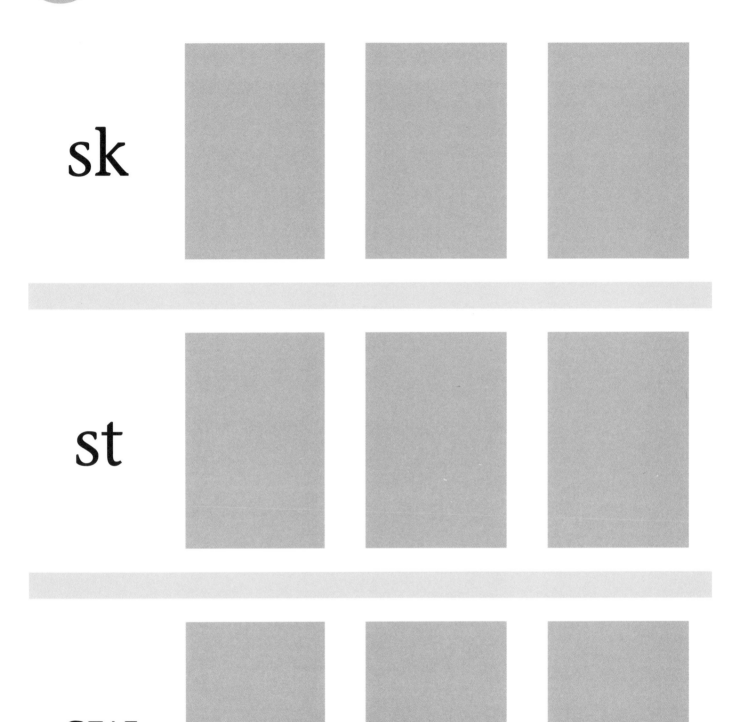

Phonics Intervention Centers
Consonant Digraphs and Blends

EMC 3522 • © Evan-Moor Corp.

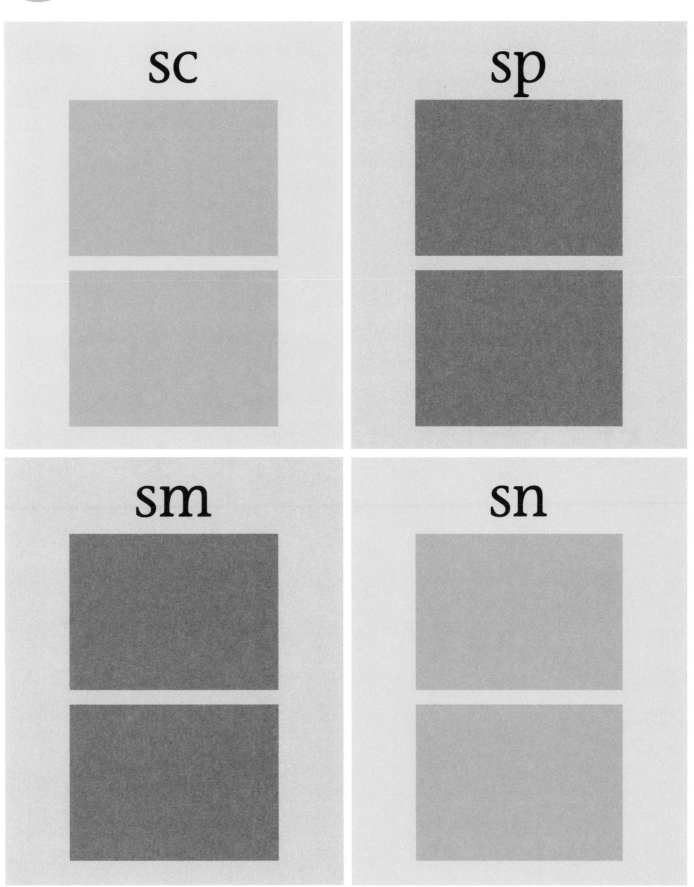

sc

sp

sm

sn

sk

st

sw

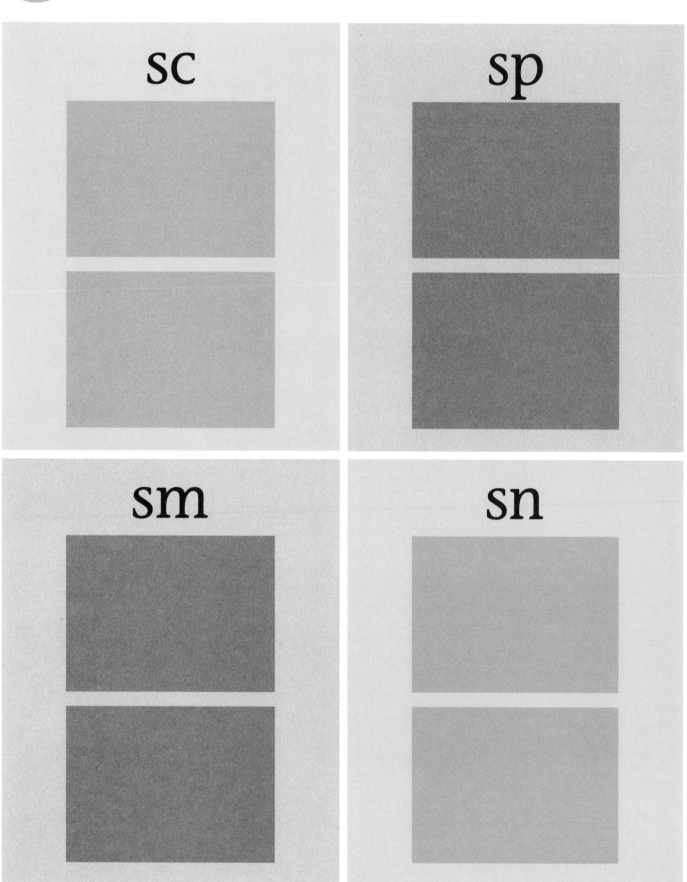

sc

sp

sm

sn

sk

st

sw

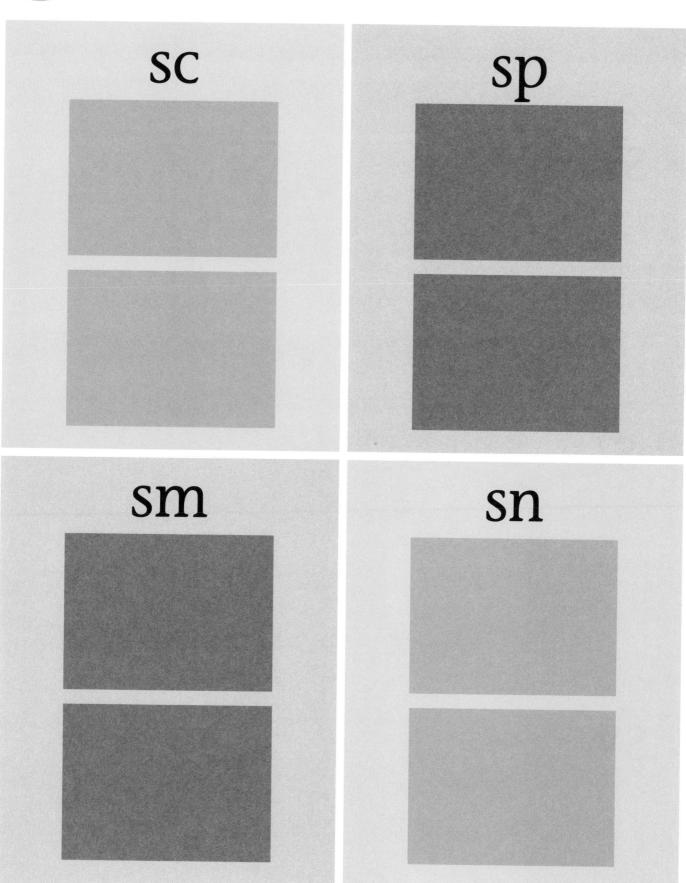

sc

sp

sm

sn

sk

st

sw

sc

sp

sm

sn

sk

st

sw

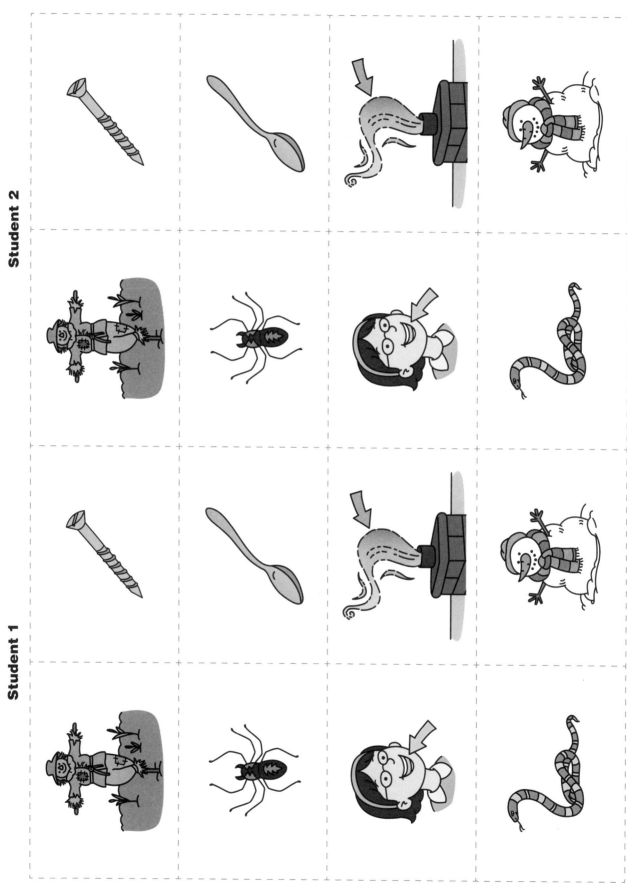

Student 2

Student 1

Student 2

EMC 3522 • Center 7 • Mat A

Student 2

EMC 3522 • Center 7 • Mat A

Student 2

EMC 3522 • Center 7 • Mat A

Student 2

EMC 3522 • Center 7 • Mat A

Student 2

EMC 3522 • Center 7 • Mat A

Student 2

EMC 3522 • Center 7 • Mat A

Student 2

EMC 3522 • Center 7 • Mat A

Student 2

EMC 3522 • Center 7 • Mat A

Student 1

EMC 3522 • Center 7 • Mat A

Student 1

EMC 3522 • Center 7 • Mat A

Student 1

EMC 3522 • Center 7 • Mat A

Student 1

EMC 3522 • Center 7 • Mat A

Student 1

EMC 3522 • Center 7 • Mat A

Student 1

EMC 3522 • Center 7 • Mat A

Student 1

EMC 3522 • Center 7 • Mat A

Student 1

EMC 3522 • Center 7 • Mat A

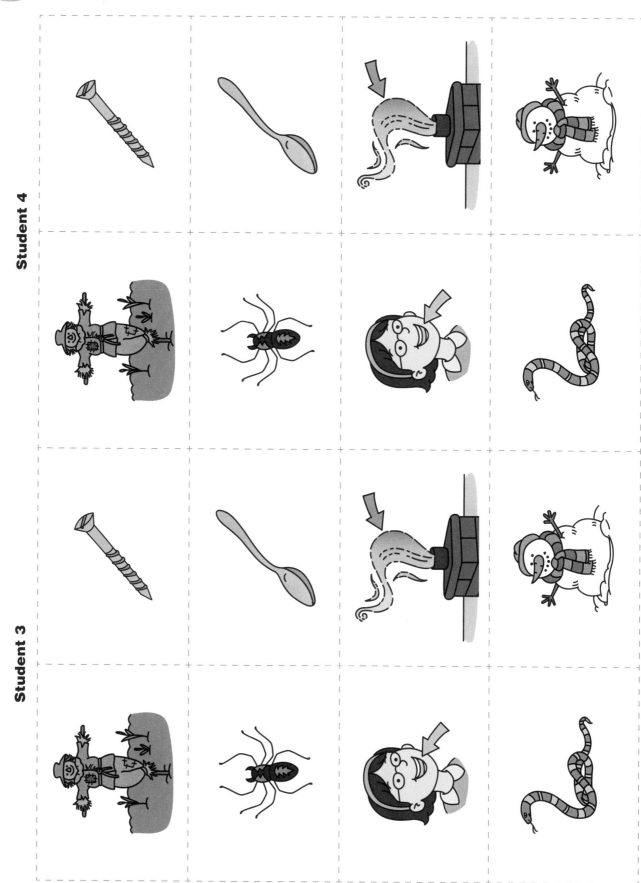

Student 4

Student 3

Student 4

EMC 3522 • Center 7 • Mat A

Student 4

EMC 3522 • Center 7 • Mat A

Student 4

EMC 3522 • Center 7 • Mat A

Student 4

EMC 3522 • Center 7 • Mat A

Student 4

EMC 3522 • Center 7 • Mat A

Student 4

EMC 3522 • Center 7 • Mat A

Student 4

EMC 3522 • Center 7 • Mat A

Student 3

EMC 3522 • Center 7 • Mat A

Student 3

EMC 3522 • Center 7 • Mat A

Student 3

EMC 3522 • Center 7 • Mat A

Student 3

EMC 3522 • Center 7 • Mat A

Student 3

EMC 3522 • Center 7 • Mat A

Student 3

EMC 3522 • Center 7 • Mat A

Student 6

Student 5

Student 6

EMC 3522 • Center 7 • Mat A

Student 6

EMC 3522 • Center 7 • Mat A

Student 6

EMC 3522 • Center 7 • Mat A

Student 6

EMC 3522 • Center 7 • Mat A

Student 6

EMC 3522 • Center 7 • Mat A

Student 6

EMC 3522 • Center 7 • Mat A

Student 6

EMC 3522 • Center 7 • Mat A

Student 6

EMC 3522 • Center 7 • Mat A

Student 5

EMC 3522 • Center 7 • Mat A

Student 5

EMC 3522 • Center 7 • Mat A

Student 5

EMC 3522 • Center 7 • Mat A

Student 5

EMC 3522 • Center 7 • Mat A

Student 5

EMC 3522 • Center 7 • Mat A

Student 5

EMC 3522 • Center 7 • Mat A

Student 5

EMC 3522 • Center 7 • Mat A

Student 5

EMC 3522 • Center 7 • Mat A

Student 2

  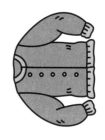

Student 1

  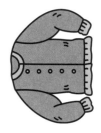

Student 2

EMC 3522
Center 7 • Mat B

Student 2

EMC 3522
Center 7 • Mat B

Student 2

EMC 3522
Center 7 • Mat B

Student 2

EMC 3522
Center 7 • Mat B

Student 2

EMC 3522
Center 7 • Mat B

Student 2

EMC 3522
Center 7 • Mat B

Student 1

EMC 3522
Center 7 • Mat B

Student 1

EMC 3522
Center 7 • Mat B

Student 1

EMC 3522
Center 7 • Mat B

Student 1

EMC 3522
Center 7 • Mat B

Student 1

EMC 3522
Center 7 • Mat B

Student 1

EMC 3522
Center 7 • Mat B

Student 4

Student 3

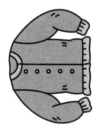

Student 4

EMC 3522
Center 7 • Mat B

Student 4

EMC 3522
Center 7 • Mat B

Student 4

EMC 3522
Center 7 • Mat B

Student 4

EMC 3522
Center 7 • Mat B

Student 4

EMC 3522
Center 7 • Mat B

Student 4

EMC 3522
Center 7 • Mat B

Student 3

EMC 3522
Center 7 • Mat B

Student 3

EMC 3522
Center 7 • Mat B

Student 4

EMC 3522
Center 7 • Mat B

Student 3

EMC 3522
Center 7 • Mat B

Student 3

EMC 3522
Center 7 • Mat B

Student 3

EMC 3522
Center 7 • Mat B

Student 3

EMC 3522
Center 7 • Mat B

Student 3

EMC 3522
Center 7 • Mat B

Student 3

EMC 3522
Center 7 • Mat B

Student 6

  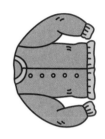

Student 5

  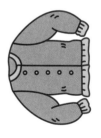

Student 6

EMC 3522
Center 7 • Mat B

Student 6

EMC 3522
Center 7 • Mat B

Student 6

EMC 3522
Center 7 • Mat B

Student 6

EMC 3522
Center 7 • Mat B

Student 6

EMC 3522
Center 7 • Mat B

Student 6

EMC 3522
Center 7 • Mat B

Student 6

EMC 3522
Center 7 • Mat B

Student 5

EMC 3522
Center 7 • Mat B

Student 5

EMC 3522
Center 7 • Mat B

Student 5

EMC 3522
Center 7 • Mat B

Student 5

EMC 3522
Center 7 • Mat B

Student 5

EMC 3522
Center 7 • Mat B

Student 5

EMC 3522
Center 7 • Mat B

Student 5

EMC 3522
Center 7 • Mat B

Practice It!

Say the word that names the picture.
Listen to the beginning sounds.
Write the two missing letters on the lines.

| sk   sm   sn   sp   st   sw |

1.

___ ___ e l l

2.

___ ___ u n k

3.

___ ___ a n

4.

___ ___ a k e

5.

___ ___ i l l

6.

___ ___ o v e

7.

___ ___ u l l

8.

___ ___ e e p

Name _____

Initial s Blends

center

7

Read It!

Write the word on the line that best completes the sentence.

1. I _____ smoke from a grill.
   smell   smile

2. Stan can _____ as fast as Stella.
   skin   swim

3. My cat Snubs is small and _____.
   sweet   sweep

4. Can you spell while you _____ rope?
   snip   skip

5. A _____ sleeps under a stone.
   skate   snake

6. I can snap this dry _____ in two.
   stack   stick

7. A rocket speeds into _____.
   space   spice

8. I will say "BOO!" to _____ my friend Steve.
   scale   scare

center

Consonant Blends Review

For the Teacher

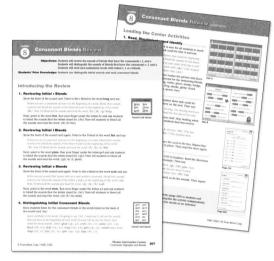

Lesson Plan

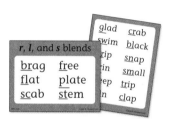

r, l, and s blends

brag	free
flat	plate
scab	stem

glad crab
swim black
rip snap
in small
eep trip
n clap

Sound Cards

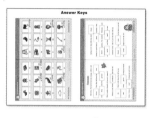

Answer Keys

For the Student

front (Mat A)

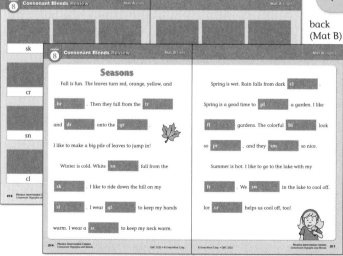

Activity Mats

To make Mat A, place pages 212 and 213 side by side and laminate. (Turn over for Mat B.)

back (Mat B)

plant
scarf

Task Cards

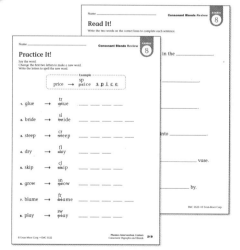

Practice and Assessment Activities

center 8

Consonant Blends Review

Objectives: Students will review the sounds of blends that have the consonants *r*, *l*, and *s*.
Students will distinguish the sounds of blends that have the consonants *r*, *l*, and *s*.
Students will read and understand words with initial *r*, *l*, or *s* blends.

Students' Prior Knowledge: Students can distinguish initial sounds and read consonant blends.

Introducing the Review

1. Reviewing Initial *r* Blends

Show the front of the sound card. Point to the *r* blend in the word **brag** and say:

*When you see a consonant and an **r** at the beginning of a word, blend their sounds.*
*Listen to me blend the sounds of the letters **b** and **r** at the beginning of this word:*
/br/. Now I'll blend all the sounds and read the word: /br/ /ă/ /g/ brag.

Next, point to the word **free**. Run your finger under the letters *f-r* and ask students
to blend the sounds that the letters stand for. (/fr/) Then tell students to blend all
the sounds and read the word. (/fr/ /ē/ free)

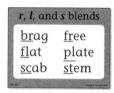

Sound Card (front)

2. Reviewing Initial *l* Blends

Show the front of the sound card again. Point to the *l* blend in the word **flat** and say:

*When you see a consonant and an **l** at the beginning of a word, blend their sounds.*
*Listen to me blend the sounds of the letters **f** and **l** at the beginning of this word:*
/fl/. Now I'll blend all the sounds and read the word: /fl/ /ă/ /t/ flat.

Next, point to the word **plate**. Run your finger under the letters *p-l* and ask students
to blend the sounds that the letters stand for. (/pl/) Then tell students to blend all
the sounds and read the word. (/pl/ /ā/ /t/ plate)

3. Reviewing Initial *s* Blends

Show the front of the sound card again. Point to the *s* blend in the word **scab** and say:

*When you see a word that begins with an **s** and another consonant, blend their sounds.*
*Listen to me blend the sounds of the letters **s** and **c** at the beginning of this word: /sk/.*
Now I'll blend all the sounds and read the word: /sk/ /ă/ /b/ scab.

Next, point to the word **stem**. Run your finger under the letters *s-t* and ask students
to blend the sounds that the letters stand for. (/st/) Then tell students to blend all
the sounds and read the word. (/st/ /ĕ/ /m/ stem)

4. Distinguishing Initial Consonant Blends

Have students listen for the consonant blends in the words listed on the back of
the sound card. Say:

Listen carefully to the words I'm going to say. First, I want you to tell me the sounds
that you hear at the beginning of each word. Second, tell me the two letters that
*stand for those sounds. Listen: **glad** (/gl/, g-l), **crab** (/kr/, c-r), **swim** (/sw/, s-w),*
***black** (/bl/, b-l), **drip** (/dr/, d-r), **snap** (/sn/, s-n), **grin** (/gr/, g-r), **small** (/sm/, s-m),*
***sleep** (/sl/, s-l), **trip** (/tr/, t-r), **spin** (/sp/, s-p), **clap** (/kl/, c-l).*

Sound Card (back)

© Evan-Moor Corp. • EMC 3522

Leading the Center Activities

1. Read, Discriminate, and Identify ....

Place Mat A on a table where it is easy for all students to reach. Then give each student four task cards for Mat A and say:

Each box on this mat has two letters that stand for beginning sounds you have learned. Let's blend the sounds for the letters in the first box: /sk/. Now look at your cards. Who has a card with the picture of a word that starts with /sk/? (The student with the picture of a skunk shows that card.)

Have the student say the word that names the picture and place the card in the box. Repeat this process for the remaining blends. (prize, blanket, swing, grapes, flag; crown, glove, stamp, bridge, plug, scarf; snowman, train, sled, frog, smoke, globe; cloud, stairs or steps, drip or drop, flower, spoon, tree)

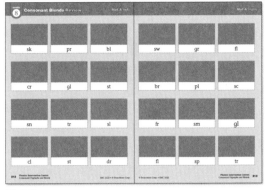

Mat A

2. Read and Understand ....

Turn over the mat and give each student three task cards for Mat B. Read aloud the title of the story on the mat. Then say:

Some of the words in this story are missing. The missing words are on your cards. Listen carefully as I read the first line of the story.

Run your finger under the words as you read. Stop reading when you get to the first blue box and tell students that this word is missing. Then say:

Let's blend the sounds for the letters in this box: /br/. Who has a card with a word that starts with /br/? (The student with the word **brown** shows that card.)

Have the student say the word and place the card in the box. Repeat this process until all the missing words are in place. Then read the story again.

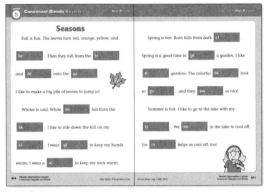

Mat B

3. Practice the Skill ....

Distribute the Practice It! activity (page 219) to students. Read the directions aloud and guide students through the example. Then say:

*Let's blend the sounds to read the first word: /gl/ /ōō/ **glue**. Now let's change the letters g-l to t-r and write the new word: t-r-u-e. Now blend the sounds and read the new word: /tr/ /ōō/ **true**.*

Tell students that as letters change in a word, so do the sounds. Then repeat this process with the remaining words.

Page 219

Apply and Assess

After the lesson, distribute the Read It! activity (page 220) to students and read the directions aloud. Have students complete the activity independently. Then listen to them read the sentences. Use the results as an informal assessment of students' skill mastery.

Page 220

r, l, and s blends

brag   fr<u>ee</u>

<u>fl</u>at   <u>pl</u>ate

<u>sc</u>ab   <u>st</u>em

Answer Keys

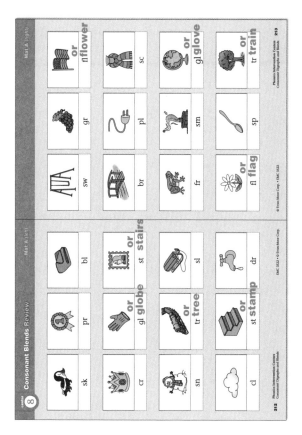

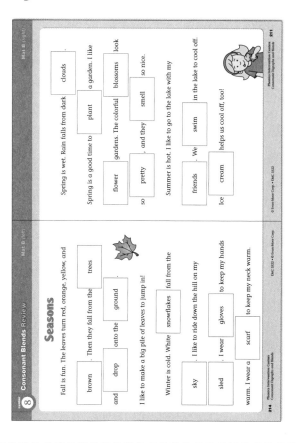

glad	crab
<u>g</u>lad	<u>cr</u>ab
<u>sw</u>im	<u>bl</u>ack
<u>dr</u>ip	<u>sn</u>ap
<u>gr</u>in	<u>sm</u>all
<u>sl</u>eep	<u>tr</u>ip
<u>sp</u>in	<u>cl</u>ap

EMC 3522   Center 8 • Sound Card

Answer Keys

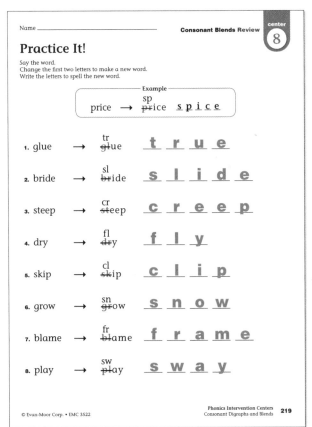

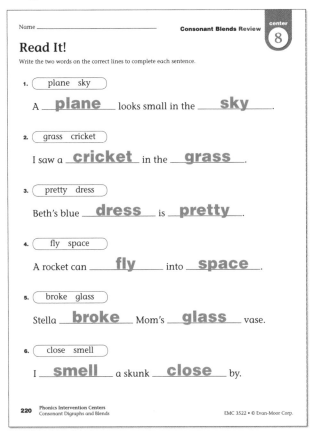

Spring is wet. Rain falls from dark cl_____.

Spring is a good time to pl_____ a garden. I like

fl_____ gardens. The colorful bl_____ look

so pr_____, and they sm_____ so nice.

Summer is hot. I like to go to the lake with my

fr_____. We sw_____ in the lake to cool off.

Ice cr_____ helps us cool off, too!

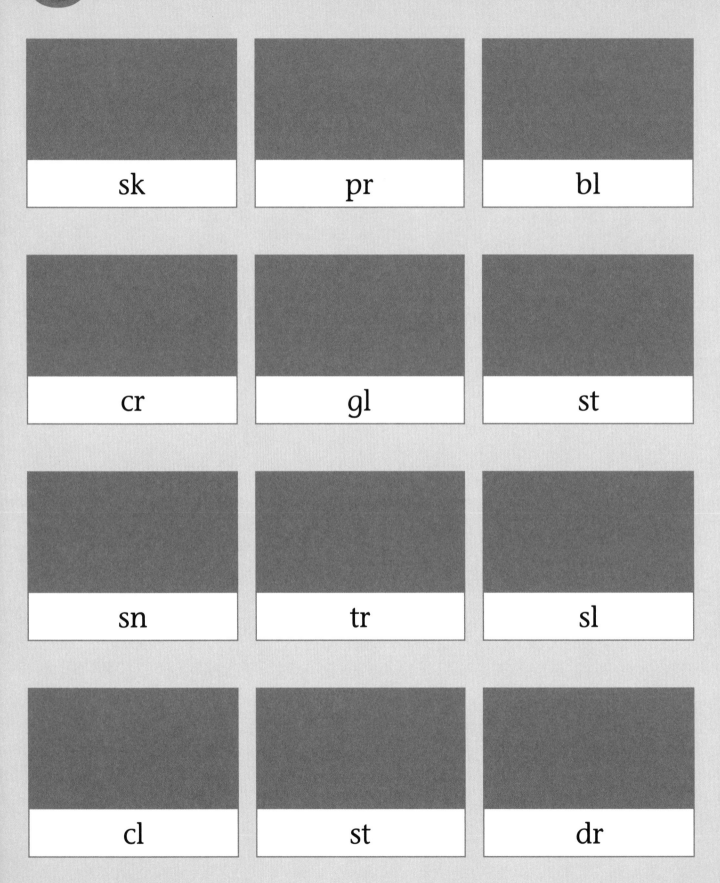

sk

pr

bl

cr

gl

st

sn

tr

sl

cl

st

dr

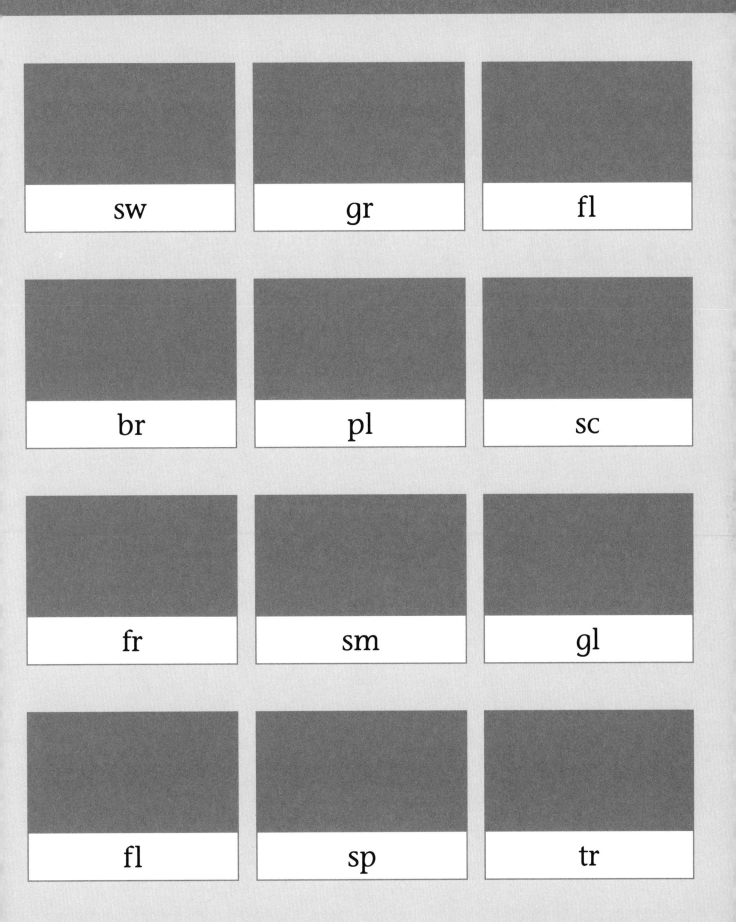

sw

gr

fl

br

pl

sc

fr

sm

gl

fl

sp

tr

Seasons

Fall is fun. The leaves turn red, orange, yellow, and

| br | . Then they fall from the | tr |

and | dr | onto the | gr | .

I like to make a big pile of leaves to jump in!

Winter is cold. White | sn | fall from the

| sk | . I like to ride down the hill on my

| sl | . I wear | gl | to keep my hands

warm. I wear a | sc | to keep my neck warm.

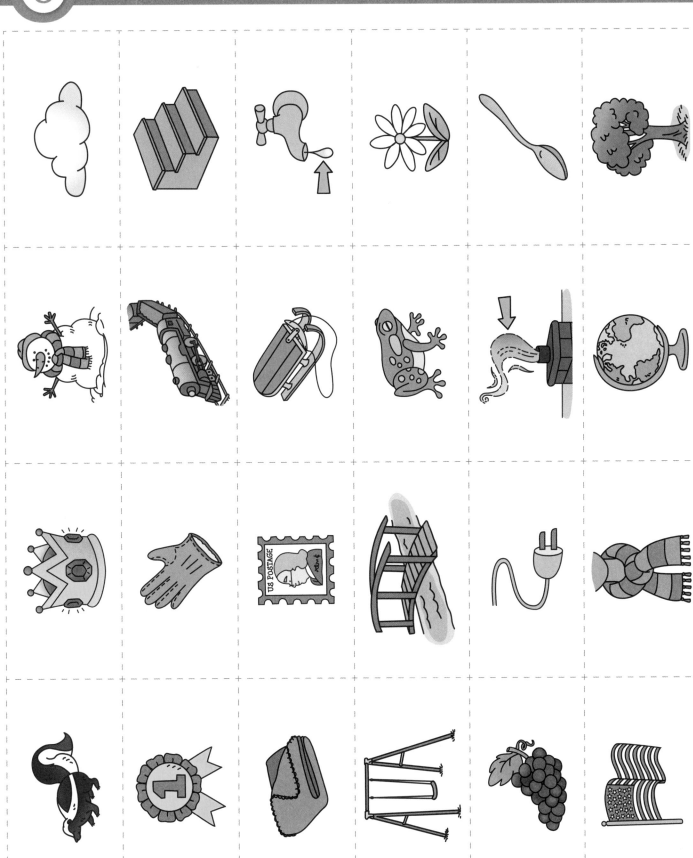

EMC 3522 • Center 8 • Mat A

EMC 3522 • Center 8 • Mat A

EMC 3522 • Center 8 • Mat A

EMC 3522 • Center 8 • Mat A

EMC 3522 • Center 8 • Mat A

EMC 3522 • Center 8 • Mat A

EMC 3522 • Center 8 • Mat A

EMC 3522 • Center 8 • Mat A

EMC 3522 • Center 8 • Mat A

EMC 3522 • Center 8 • Mat A

EMC 3522 • Center 8 • Mat A

EMC 3522 • Center 8 • Mat A

EMC 3522 • Center 8 • Mat A

EMC 3522 • Center 8 • Mat A

EMC 3522 • Center 8 • Mat A

EMC 3522 • Center 8 • Mat A

EMC 3522 • Center 8 • Mat A

EMC 3522 • Center 8 • Mat A

Phonics Intervention Centers
Consonant Digraphs and Blends

clouds	plant	flower
blossoms	pretty	smell
friends	swim	cream
brown	trees	drop
ground	snowflakes	sky
sled	gloves	scarf

EMC 3522
Center 8 • Mat B

EMC 3522
Center 8 • Mat B

EMC 3522
Center 8 • Mat B

EMC 3522
Center 8 • Mat B

EMC 3522
Center 8 • Mat B

EMC 3522
Center 8 • Mat B

EMC 3522
Center 8 • Mat B

EMC 3522
Center 8 • Mat B

EMC 3522
Center 8 • Mat B

EMC 3522
Center 8 • Mat B

EMC 3522
Center 8 • Mat B

EMC 3522
Center 8 • Mat B

EMC 3522
Center 8 • Mat B

EMC 3522
Center 8 • Mat B

EMC 3522
Center 8 • Mat B

EMC 3522
Center 8 • Mat B

EMC 3522
Center 8 • Mat B

EMC 3522
Center 8 • Mat B

Practice It!

Say the word.
Change the first two letters to make a new word.
Write the letters to spell the new word.

> **Example**
>
> sp
> price → ~~pr~~ice   s p i c e

tr
1. glue → ~~g~~lue   ___ ___ ___ ___

sl
2. bride → ~~br~~ide   ___ ___ ___ ___ ___

cr
3. steep → ~~st~~eep   ___ ___ ___ ___ ___

fl
4. dry → ~~dr~~y   ___ ___ ___

cl
5. skip → ~~sk~~ip   ___ ___ ___ ___

sn
6. grow → ~~gr~~ow   ___ ___ ___ ___

fr
7. blame → ~~bl~~ame   ___ ___ ___ ___ ___

sw
8. play → ~~pl~~ay   ___ ___ ___ ___

Read It!

Write the two words on the correct lines to complete each sentence.

1. (plane   sky)

   A _____ looks small in the _____.

2. (grass   cricket)

   I saw a _____ in the _____.

3. (pretty   dress)

   Beth's blue _____ is _____.

4. (fly   space)

   A rocket can _____ into _____.

5. (broke   glass)

   Stella _____ Mom's _____ vase.

6. (close   smell)

   I _____ a skunk _____ by.

Provide students with important reading and language arts skill practice!

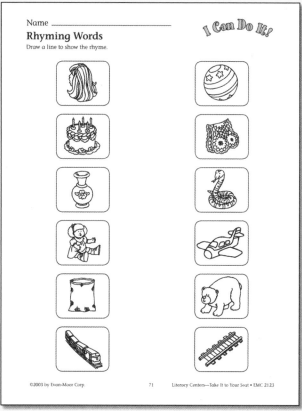

Take it to Your Seat
Literacy Centers

Grade	
PreK-K	EMC 2401
K–1	EMC 2123
1–3	EMC 788
2–3	EMC 2723
3–4	EMC 2124
4–5	EM1 2724
4–6	EM1 2719

Features:

• Provide students with important reading and language arts skill practice that feels more like fun than work!

• Each book comes with up to 18 self-contained centers that students can pick up and take anywhere.

• They're a perfect way to provide students with the extra practice they need to strengthen language skills.

Help your child master math skills!

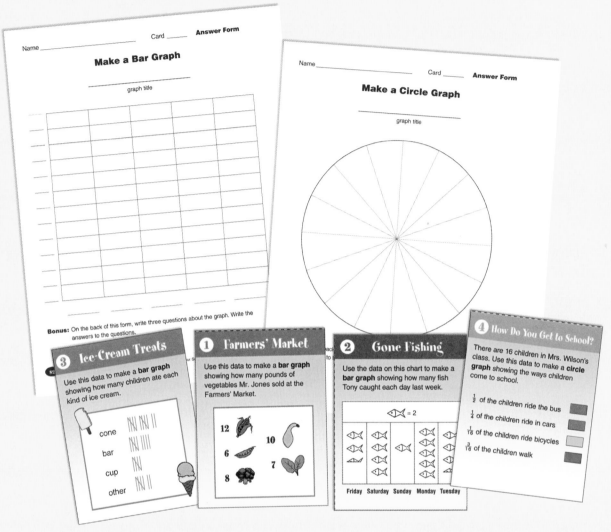

Make a Bar Graph

Name _____

Card ____ Answer Form

graph title

Bonus: On the back of this form, write three questions about the graph. Write the answers to the questions.

Make a Circle Graph

Name _____

Card ____ Answer Form

graph title

3 Ice-Cream Treats

Use this data to make a **bar graph** showing how many children ate each kind of ice cream.

cone	‖‖ ‖‖ ‖
	‖‖ ‖‖‖
bar	
	‖‖
cup	‖‖
other	‖‖ ‖

1 Farmers' Market

Use this data to make a **bar graph** showing how many pounds of vegetables Mr. Jones sold at the Farmers' Market.

12   10

6   7

8

2 Gone Fishing

Use the data on this chart to make a **bar graph** showing how many fish Tony caught each day last week.

= 2

Friday Saturday Sunday Monday Tuesday

4 How Do You Get to School?

There are 16 children in Mrs. Wilson's class. Use this data to make a **circle graph** showing the ways children come to school.

$\frac{1}{2}$ of the children ride the bus

$\frac{1}{4}$ of the children ride in cars

$\frac{1}{16}$ of the children ride bicycles

$\frac{3}{16}$ of the children walk

Features:

- Aligned with NCTM Standards.

- Provide fun, hands-on activities.

- Help students master numbers and operations, algebra, geometry, measurement, data analysis, and probability

- 192 full-color pages.

Take it to Your Seat
Math Centers

Grade

K–1	EMC 3020
1–3	EMC 3013
2–3	EMC 3021
3–4	EMC 3022
4–6	EM1 3012

Grades 3–4   Correlated to State Standards

- 15 full-color centers
- Math topics: measurement, graphing, fractions & decimals, range, mode, median, perimeter & area, solid shapes, and more

Take It to Your Seat
Math Centers
GRADES
3-4

Evan-Moor
EMC 3022

Enrich any core writing or language arts program!

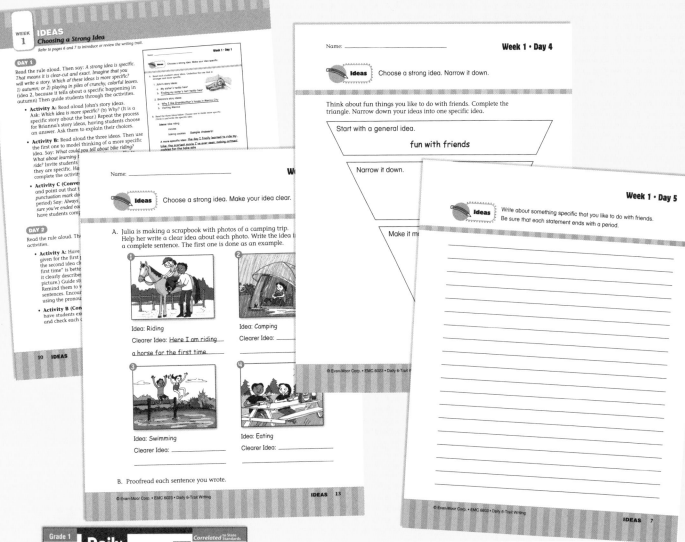

Daily 6-Trait Writing	
Grade	
1	EMC 6021
2	EMC 6022
3	EMC 6023
4	EMC 6024
5	EMC 6025
6+	EMC 6026

Features:

- 125 scaffolded, trait-based writing lessons

- A trait-based writing rubric

- Teacher pages that include an easy-to-follow teaching path and ideas for modeling and eliciting student responses

- Activities that cover narrative, expository, descriptive, and persuasive writing

Daily Language Review

Help build your child's language skills!

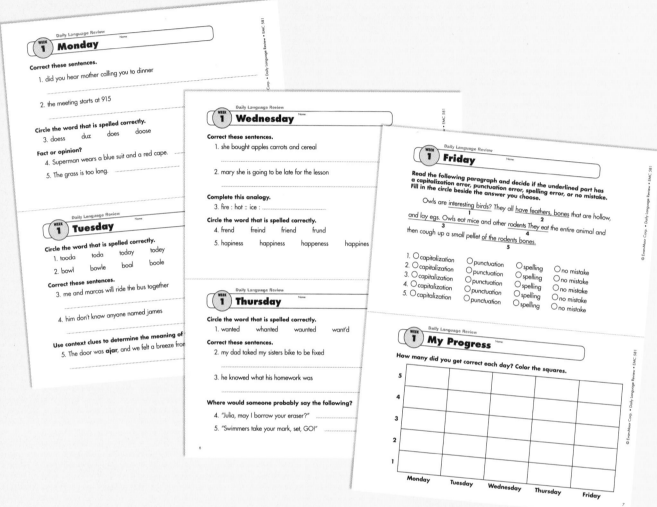

Repeated, focused, practice in:

- sentence editing

- corrections in punctuation, capitalization, spelling, grammar, and vocabulary

- additional activities that cover a wide range of language and reading skills

Daily Language Review

Grade

1	EMC 579
2	EMC 580
3	EMC 581
4	EMC 582
5	EMC 583
6	EMC 576
7	EMC 2797
8	EMC 2798